Collecting
Seashells

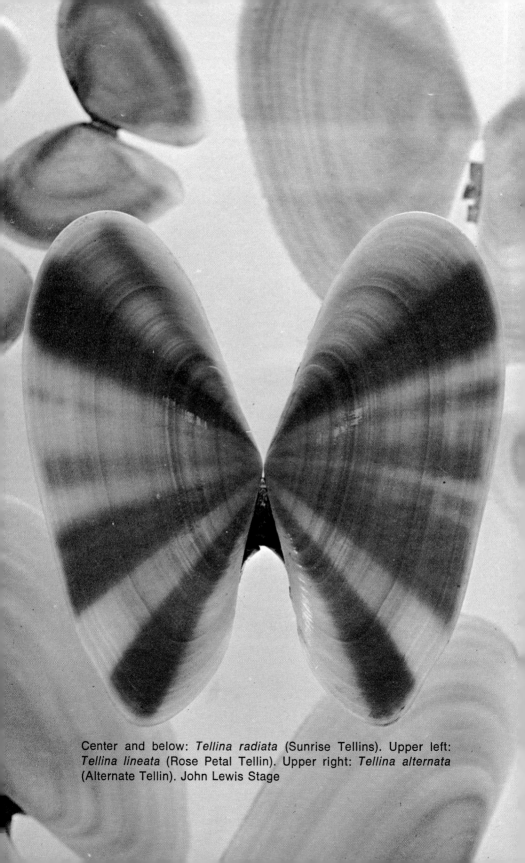

Center and below: *Tellina radiata* (Sunrise Tellins). Upper left: *Tellina lineata* (Rose Petal Tellin). Upper right: *Tellina alternata* (Alternate Tellin). John Lewis Stage

Collecting
Seashells

Kathleen Yerger Johnstone

GROSSET & DUNLAP
A NATIONAL GENERAL COMPANY
PUBLISHERS / NEW YORK

The color plates, black-and-white photographs and pen-and-ink drawings used in the book are by courtesy of the following: JOHN LEWIS STAGE Frontispiece; facing page 36, facing page 68, facing page 160. WILLIAM M. STEPHENS Pages 69, 78, 79, facing page 1, 124 (bottom), facing page 130. HARRY INGE JOHNSTONE Pages 23, 26 (after Dall), 43, 55, 62, 67, 82, 85, 100 (top, after Clench), 108 (after Kohn), 115, 116, 124 (top). THE ACADEMY OF NATURAL SCIENCES, PHILADELPHIA Pages 98–99 (from *Indo-Pacific Mollusca,* Vol. 1, No. 1, Introduction); Page 133 (from *Indo-Pacific Mollusca*); Pages 140–141 (from *Indo-Pacific Mollusca,* modified from J. Demond, 1957). A. AND C. BLACK LTD., LONDON Page 128 (after Schiemenz, from *Mollusca,* Vol. 5, "A Treatise on Zoology"). S. C. HOLLISTER Page 144. THE JOHNSTONE COLLECTION Pages 25, 170. KIENER AND FISCHER (1837–1880) Pages 126, 127. THE MUSEUM OF COMPARATIVE ZOOLOGY, HARVARD UNIVERSITY From *Johnsonia,* Pages 7, 12 (after d'Orbigny, 1847, *Voyage dans L'Amérique Méridionale*), 15, 30, 86 (left), 86 (right), 117, 118, 119, 137, 153, 154, 158 Endsheets. THE NATIONAL ACADEMY OF SCIENCES Page 100 (bottom, after Dr. Allan J. Kohn and Miss Marion Adachi, from *Proceedings,* 1956); Pages 104–105 (photographs from a moving picture made by Dr. Alan J. Kohn with assistance from Mr. Charles E. Cutress, from *Proceedings,* 1956, with the permission of Dr. Kohn). *Natural History* Pages 14, 26, 40. Photographs by the Author Pages 47, 66, 143.

Foreword

This book is dedicated to the professional malacologists who have been unfailingly gracious to us from the start, when we were such rank amateurs. Their help, never even tinged with condescension, encouraged us to try to develop a point of view about collecting more in line with theirs than many amateurs attain.

They are, in the order in which we met them,

Dr. Harald A. Rehder, Curator of the Mollusk Department, United States National Museum;

Dr. R. Tucker Abbott, then an Associate Curator at the U. S. N. M., and now holding the Pilsbry Chair of Malacology of the Academy of Natural Sciences, of Philadelphia;

Dr. Joseph P. E. Morrison, Associate Curator of the U. S. N. M.

These three professionals welcomed us in the department, and Dr. Abbott showed us how the famous collection is housed, pulling out drawers with specimens of special interest; introduced us to a young man who was cataloging specimens, and asked him to demonstrate his meticulous work; took us in the library and brought out some of its rare old volumes and, waving his hand to men at various tables, whispered, "Research students, native and foreign." When we left, Dr. Rehder presented us with a list of books and publications with checks by those he thought would be most helpful.

We did not know then that such red-carpet treatment was exceptional. It has to be, otherwise the scientists would spend their time conducting tours and neglecting their researches.

As the only coastal Alabama subscribers to *Johnsonia,* a series of scholarly monographs published by the Museum of Comparative Zoology, we were selected as laymen who might be helpful to a student making a survey of the whole Gulf coast. Thomas A. Pulley, then a candidate for his doctorate, now Director of the Houston Museum of Natural Science, came to see our collection of local material and to get directions to good collecting spots.

"Can you stay for dinner?" changed to "Do spend the night!" Tom beamed at the invitation to dinner on a table instead of from a can; and looked dreamy at the prospect of a night in a bed instead of on the padded board spanning the car seats which, on this field trip skirting the Gulf, served as his resting place. A real dinner and a real bed were treats not to be rejected.

But there was little time to enjoy the bed. Sensing our eagerness to learn, he talked on and on, charming us: dazzling us with new ideas; painting future possibilities in glowing color. In short—proselyting.

He aroused our interest in the species of our own coast by telling us that there was still much information needed about them and about the whole area; that although the Gulf of Mexico could not be called a virgin territory, it was without question a fertile field for further scientific investigation; and that we, as laymen living here with almost unlimited opportunity for observation and exploration, could really make contributions of value to the study of malacology.

Imagine fielding for the "pros"! That idea had never occurred to us. It gave stature to this business of shell collecting, which until then we had simply considered a pleasant pastime. We could see that he was in earnest; and before he left he had given us specific suggestions about how we could begin to help. He had touched the right chord. This idea gave us a goal toward which to strive; it gave direction and purpose to our activities.

When Tom saw some of the shells we were in the process of cleaning, his eyes gleamed. "Where from? When?" And when he had the answer he said, "These should go to Harvard for study. These are new, valid subspecies, I am sure. Will you lend the series?"

Of course! So he passed us on to his internationally recognized chiefs, Dr. William J. Clench, Curator of the Mollusk Department at Harvard's Museum of Comparative Zoology; and his associate, Dr. Ruth D. Turner. Shells and letters flew back and forth. And, in the following years, Bill and Ruth, as they became, stopped by often to see us on their way to or from meetings or judging shell shows; or for a respite during arduous field trips collecting in fresh water streams of Southern swamps.

Tucker, no longer "Dr. Abbott," came with them once; and students twice: Ken, who was also as interested in birds as we were; and Don, from "down under," not so jaded by the wonders of the greatest coral reef on earth at his front door, that he couldn't have the time of his life shelling in an Alabama inlet. Today these students are Dr. Kenneth Boss, Assistant Curator of Mollusks, of the Museum of Comparative Zoology, and Dr. Donald F. McMichael, Director of Conservation for Australia. Of them all, we are most indebted to Ruth and Bill, who have guided our learning over the years and have helped to mold our philosophy.

Acknowledgments

I wish to acknowledge with gratitude the help given me in the preparation of this book.

I am indebted to Drs. William J. Clench, former curator, and Ruth D. Turner, of the Mollusk Department of the Museum of Comparative Zoology, at Harvard University, for reading the manuscript and making helpful suggestions;

To the editors of *Holiday* for permission to use parts of the material from my article for the *Holiday Handbook: Collecting Seashells,* July, 1966;

To George and Mary Kline, of Madison, New Jersey, for lending me the field notes of their expeditions to Ceylon and New Caledonia; for the less technical records of all of their adventurous collecting trips; for long discussions by our fireside over a cold, rainy Thanksgiving weekend about their collecting techniques and their ideas about the sort of book needed for novice collectors;

To Elizabeth Blair Grigg, of Brisbane, Australia, for sending me a copy of her collecting log covering twenty years of collecting on the Great Barrier Reef and coasts of Australia, New Guinea, New Britain, and the Admiralty Islands; and for her introduction to William S. Grant to whom I am indebted for several letters describing the highlights of his years of collecting on the Great Barrier Reef;

To John C. Finlay, Newark, Delaware; Helen Bonadies, Miami, Florida; Mrs. Jeanne Frisby, Port Isabel, Texas; Mrs. Elsie Marshall, Seattle, Washington; Robert C. Work, Oceanographic Institute, Miami; and Señor Pedro de Mesa, Philippine Islands; for permission to quote from letters about their collecting experiences;

To Dr. Clench, as editor of *Johnsonia,* Monographs of Western Atlantic Mollusks, published by the Department of Mollusks of the Museum of Comparative Zoology, for permission to reproduce many plates from *Johnsonia;*

To Dr. Ernst Mayr, Director of the Museum of Comparative Zoology, Harvard University, for permission to reproduce the engraving from *Historia Naturale di Ferrante;*

·To Dr. R. Tucker Abbott, editor of *Indo-Pacific Mollusca* published by the Department of Mollusks, Academy of Natural Sciences, Philadelphia, for permission to reproduce three drawings;

To Dr. Henning Lemche and Dr. T. Wolff, Universitetets Zoologiski Museum, Copenhagen, for permission to copy the photographs and original drawings of *Neopilina galatheae* made by the late Dr. Anton Brunn, leader of the Galathea Expedition, and his staff artist, the late P. Winther, on page 27.

To the publishing firm of Angus and Robertson (UK) Ltd. for permission to use our drawing of *Melo amphora* made from a photograph by T. C. Roughley for his excellent book *Wonders of the Great Barrier Reef;*

To Adam and Charles Black, Ltd., London, for permission to reproduce the Figure 49 of *Natica josephina* from *Mollusca,* Vol. 5 of *A Treatise on Zoology,* 1906, by P. Pelseneer, edited by Ray Lancaster;

To *Natural History* for permission to reproduce drawings from "The Need to Classify" by Dr. R. L. Batten, March 1958;

To Dr. Alan Kohn, Department of Zoology, University of Washington, Seattle, for allowing me to copy the freehand drawings he made for me of the *Conus* feeding on a worm; and for the seven photographs showing a *Conus* attacking and swallowing a fish;

To The National Academy of Sciences, Washington, D. C., for permission to reproduce the drawing of *Conus striatus* and the five photographs which appeared in Dr. Kohn's paper published in *Proceedings* Vol. 42, No. 3, March 1956;

To Dean S. C. Hollister, of Cornell University, for the photographs he made of *Busycon contrarium* laying an egg case;

To the staff of The Mobile Public Library for assistance in obtaining any material needed;

To Christine Brabner and Beth Pollard for their skill in deciphering and typing the handwritten draft; and for catching errors which had escaped other eyes.

My greatest indebtedness is due my husband, who is not only my partner in the field but my editor-in-residence. His constructive criticism has been invaluable in planning the scope, tone and content of the whole book; and the details of each chapter. Without his meticulous reading of each draft, correcting punctuation and spelling (often erratic), and suggesting rephrasing for clarity, this book might never have appeared.

I am further indebted to him for the drawings used as chapter ends, which I particularly wanted as decorative illustration.

Contents

Argonauta argo (Living Common Paper Argonaut); in aquarium. William M. Stephens

Chapter 1
The Shell Game

Thousands of people around the world find shell collecting a fascinating hobby, and many of these people live in North America. Some of the most enthusiastic collectors are as young as nine; some are nearing ninety. At any age the lure of finding and keeping beautiful seashells can be irresistible.

Some of these collectors are amateurs, beginners, whatever their ages; and unfortunately many of them will never graduate from that class. On the other hand, there are collectors so well informed about the branch of science concerning seashells, and so skilled in knowing how and where to find them and why they are found in some places and not in others, that such collectors should not be called "amateurs." This term is used to distinguish them from formally trained scientists, *malacologists* (măl̄á-cŏl'ŏ-gı̆sts), as the professionals in this field are called. There are about a thousand professional malacologists. "Serious laymen" is a better name for the top-ranking amateurs.

There are about thirty-six clubs of shell collectors scattered over our fifty states and Canada. Memberships include both amateurs and professionals. The clubs have interesting meetings featuring moving pictures, slide-showings with talks by people who have returned from shell-collecting trips, shell exhibits, exchange or "swap" nights, books reviews, and field trips. Some of the programs and trips are planned especially for beginners.

Amateurs enjoy describing themselves as "shell shocked." They wander through the years in a happy daze, collecting shells; talking and reading about shells; and exchanging shells with people at home and in foreign lands.

Some amateurs compare their hobby with playing a game. It is an especially good game because "winning" is not always the result of skill and years of experience. Certainly skilled collectors are successful more consistently than those with less experience, but the once-in-a-lifetime lucky break may befall anyone at any time. The excitement of that possibility never dies.

Another appealing aspect of the game is that it can be played so many different ways and the players can switch so easily from one way to another when circumstances permit. An armchair collector can become an active one; an active one, confined to an armchair for a while, or even forever, can still play the shell game with zest.

This book is written for both kinds of collectors. It is planned to help beginners become better collectors. All that helps the active collector will prepare the armchair collectors to make the most of their opportunity when the time comes.

No. 1

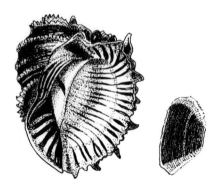

Chapter 2
Wander into
a New World

Most people become shell collectors by accident. They wander into a new world by simply walking down some beautiful beach. It has happened that way time and again.

The first sights, smells and sounds of the seashore are unforgettable. The beach blazes in the sun, the sea sparkles with its flickering lights. There is the salty smell of the sea; the pungent smell of hot sand and seaweed banked against graying driftwood; the fragrant smell of sun-warmed trees. There is the sound of the waves—racing, rolling, booming, and then breaking into fringe of foam and shower of crystal drops. Or the sound may be a soft swish as the waves break gently against the sand, spangling it with tiny bubbles. There is the sound of the wind whispering in pines and rattling stiff palm fronds.

In the distance the beach and bordering trees melt into the blues and purples of the sea and sky.

Running down the beach, a ridge of dark sea wrack and white shells may mark the crest of storm tides. Between the ridge and frothing waves, the sand is strewn with shells. Among the thousands that are bleached as bones, there are others of brilliant color: a wave-filled bowl rimmed with yellow; a fluted scoop enameled with rose; a wing of pearly-blue, sand-frosted; a crimson cone; a saffron spindle; an alabaster ear; a tiny beaded top with spiral bands of beige; an elfin cap; a pink fan ribbed with red; a sea-purple globe; a stony tendril of honey-brown.

The lovely shapes and colors catch your eye. You pause to marvel, stoop for a closer look—and then pick up. Such treasures cannot be passed by, nor once picked up, tossed away.

Back at your base, you spread your shells on a table. One by one you turn them to admire the curve or the color, or to brush away

3

the sand. You feel like King Midas gloating over his gold or like Aladdin breathless in the gem-filled cave.

Happy as you are with what you have, like most treasure hunters you want more. You are already thinking of the beauties still lying on the beach, which are yours for the taking—tomorrow.

That beach or another will lure you back soon. Entirely by chance, like countless casual strollers, you have become a bewitched beachcomber—a shell collector.

No. 2

Chapter 3
What You Can
Discover by Yourself

Pretend there is no one around who can tell you anything about your shells, not what kinds they are nor their names. Pretend there are no books at hand to explain your discoveries. Pretend you are a detective and see what you can find out for yourself just by using your eyes.

Unless you have picked up a good many shells that are exactly alike, and thus of one particular kind, each of your shells will seem to be entirely different from the others. With a little more looking you will discover that there are certain similarities.

The keenest observer will see that most of the shells, and perhaps all of them, can be separated into two groups: those made of *two* pieces hinged together, and those made of *one* piece. Some of the one-piece shells look like little "Chinese hats"; some like tiny boats with half a deck; but most of them are coiled in some way.

When you have separated the two groups, you may find there are some leftovers. It is easy to see, however, that these single shells were once part of a pair. They are separate now because the hinges are broken. They belong in the pile of shells that are still hinged.

Before putting the singles aside you may examine the broken hinges because nearly all of us are curious about the way things are put together and how they work.

You find that the hinges are not alike. Some hinge-lines are almost as straight as if drawn with a ruler; others are curved in varying degrees. Some of the hinge-lines are set with projections like ridges, hooks, or teeth. Looking at the hinged specimens, you see that the projections on one half of the pair would fit neatly into corresponding sockets or grooves of the other half. They would interlock and hold the two halves together.

You may try forcing a pair of shells to shut and, in doing so, break a brittle kind of "scab" on the outside of the shells which you had not noticed before. You prove to yourself, however, that the "teeth" do interlock; and you guess that the brittle bit may be part of the hinge device. Perhaps soaked in water it might be soft enough to stretch when the two shells closed.

In the hinge-line of one of the singles you may have noticed a triangular pit filled with black material rather like dried rubber. Among your hinged specimens you find a pair of shells joined together with a black arc, like a rubber tube, whose ends are imbedded in a triangular pit. Again you experiment. You find you can close, or nearly close, this pair of shells without breaking the black arc. You find it is like a spring which pushes the two sides apart when you stop pressing them together. If this were dry enough, it might break just like the scabby part on the outside. The single shell with this kind of hinge seems to prove that it would.

It doesn't matter that you don't know the names of these parts. What does matter is that you have discovered for yourself that there are several different ways of hinging two shells together.

You find as much variety in the shells as in their hinges. There are some with both sides alike in shape as well as color pattern or the ribs, ridges, or rings ornamenting the outside. With others the two sides are different. Some differ in color only, some differ in shape. You may have found a shell with a cupped bottom and a flat, lid-like top.

Among those with sides alike, some are very flat while others are

These specimens have been selected to show some of the many variations and the great beauty of gastropod spirals.

Top, left: Epitonium babylonium *(Tower of Babel Staircase Shell). About 1¼ inches. From deep water off Charleston, South Carolina (No. 1) and Cuba. The two specimens look different because the magnification of the specimen to the right, No. 2, is doubled to show the fine well-developed angles on the shoulder of each whorl.*

Top, right: Columbarium brayi *(Bray's Columbarium or Pagoda Shell). About 2 inches. Both from deep water off Venezuela. The long "stem" is the siphonal canal. The name* Columbarium *comes from an old Latin word meaning "dovecote."*

Bottom, left, profile: Calliostoma occidentale *(Occidental Top Shell) Right, view of the base. Less than 1 inch. Found from 6 to 980 fathoms. Western Atlantic: off Nova Scotia and south to New Jersey. Eastern Atlantic: off Finland, Shetland and Orkney Islands, and northern Scotland.*

so fat that the single sides look like little bowls, spoons and saucers. Fitted together, the two halves make a plump form. Viewed from the sides where the rims meet, some of the shells look just like the hearts on valentines.

On the inside of many of the hinged shells you notice two spots rather like scars. They are not always alike in shape, but they are always near the outer edge of the hinge-line. A faint line running just inside the rim of the shell, often connects the two scars. Sometimes the line connecting the scars has a deep indentation in it, sometimes a shallow one.

At the moment you don't know what the line and the scars mean. You can't think of a reason for them; but, being a good detective, you have noticed them. In time you plan to find out why they are there.

Looking for clues in the coiled shells of the other group you untwist them in your imagination and make an important discovery: all of these shells are hollow *cones*. Some are long and thin, some shorter and broader, some squat and wide at the base; but *all* are *cones*, open at the base, pointed at the top.

If you have seen this similarity among the many kinds of shells in this group you have made excellent progress.

Now, still in your imagination, you let each of them go. What happens? Each cone twists back into shape. Some coil tightly and steeply so that the shell is a slender spiral, pointed at the top and with the opening at the bottom. Others coil rather like a watch spring so that the opening is on the side of the shell. With such shells the coiling can only be seen at the top. On the sides, whether flat or rounded, there is no trace of the spiral.

Among those with long-drawn out coils you can trace the spiral from top to bottom. Sometimes just a minor groove marks the division between each coil. In some, one coil overlaps the one above so that a kind of rounded "shoulder," or a flat ramp marks the spiral and gives the shell an interesting shape.

If you are lucky, some of your shells will be broken so that you can see inside. In each you will find the spiral column around which the shell coils, increasing in size with each full turn.

Adding up your discoveries you will find that you can describe in a sentence all the shells in this group: most of them are made of one cone-shaped piece of shell which is coiled in some way.

Perhaps one of the spiral shells will remind you of something familiar—a snail you have found in your garden, or under a log in the woods, or in a pond. The one from the beach may not look exactly like the one from the garden, woods or pond, but enough like it to make you wonder if your beach shell is also a snail. If one of these spiraled shells is a snail, then perhaps all of them are snails.

If you have made any of these discoveries or guesses just by looking carefully at your shells, you have made a good start in being a shell collector. It is time now for an experienced shell collector to tell you how keen your observations were, how important your discoveries, and how good your guessing.

No. 3

Chapter 4
What Is a Seashell?

Those of you who saw the resemblance between one of the beach shells and a snail found in a garden or pond, may have known already that the seashells you picked up were once alive. Those of you who remembered that oysters and scallops are often called shell-*fish*, may also have guessed that these other shells were the hard parts of some kind of shellfish—a living creature.

But those of you who have lived in crowded cities where there are few gardens or parks; and far from woods, lakes and the seashore; may be very much surprised to learn that seashells were ever alive.

You saw no sign of life in those you picked up because most of the shells found on beaches are dead. Some die in the sea or are killed before they wash ashore. Their soft parts decay or are eaten by other animals. Some of the shells may have been alive when they washed up but were soon eaten by sea birds or other creatures, or dried and died in the sun and air.

Seashells belong to an enormous group of animals without backbones: the invertebrates. The particular division, *phylum* (fī'lŭm), to which seashells belong is called *Mollusca*. Individuals are called molluscs or mollusks. The name is spelled both ways. It means: soft-bodied.

Usually these soft animals are protected by some kind of hard cover, the shell. There are interesting exceptions to this generality. The shell, whatever its shape, is built up by a rapidly hardening secretion, mainly of calcium carbonate, produced by a modified part of the body wall, a fleshy lining called the *mantle*. Specialized parts of the mantle form the sculptural parts of the shell—the ribs, ridges, flanges, knobs and spines that ornament many species. Other parts of the mantle produce color patterns. The mantle of some mollusks produces a secretion which becomes glossy when it hardens. The shell, covered with coat after coat of this substance, looks like the

10

finest china. Often the mantle produces a protective outer coat which is called the *periostracum* (pĕr-ĭ-ŏs′trȧ-cŭm) and may look like varnish, fur, fiber or matted hair.

With some species the mantle covers only part of the shell; with others it can cover all of the shell. The parts of the shell covered with the mantle most of the time are kept free of encrustations which frequently coat the rest of the shell.

The mantle itself is often exquisite. It may be opaque or transparent; it may glow with changing colors; it may shine like silver. With some species it may be patterned with colorful dots, or spots, or stripes. Some mantles are edged with a fringe of waving tentacles; others are covered with filaments or protuberances which can expand and contract. They may stand erect and wave about gracefully. When they contract they may look like little bumps.

Some of the illustrations in this book were chosen to show examples of these beautiful mantles or the interesting sculpture, color patterns and outer coats produced by them.

You were quite right in separating the shells of one piece from those made of two, hinged pieces. So do the scientists.

And you were right in thinking that all the twisted beach shells might be snails. They are. Some live in the salt water of the open sea or in the less salty, brackish water of bays and lagoons. They should be called marine snails to distinguish them from the other snails which live in freshwater or on the land. Wherever they live, they are alike in basic ways, and for that reason they are all grouped together in what scientists call a *class*.

You can never go wrong in calling your coiled shells marine snails, but they have two other names which you may use and should know. One of them is UNIVALVE (uni-valve). Perhaps you know that *uni* means *one*. Think of some words beginning with *uni*. There is *uni*form, one particular kind of suit or dress. If we sing in *uni*son we sing together, as one. To *uni*fy a group of people means to make them *one*, joined together, or *united* for some purpose.

All of your snails being made of *one* piece of shell are, therefore, *uni*valves. Scientists use the word "valve" instead of "shell."

It is easy to understand now why the shells made of two parts, hinged together, are called BIVALVES (bi-valves). *Bi* means *two*. to *bi*sect an object, means to cut it into two parts. You can think of many words starting with *bi* meaning *two* of something: *bi*ped, (two feet), *bi*cycle (two wheels).

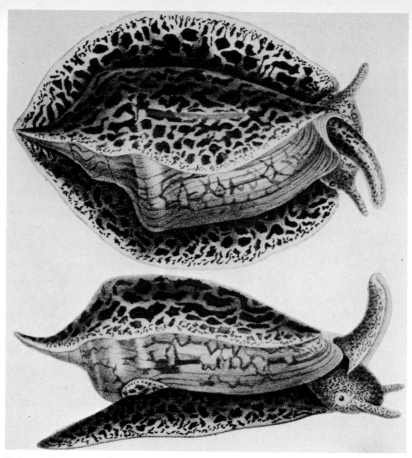

Zidona dufresnei (*Dufresne's Zidona*). This west Atlantic volute of South America is of interest for several reasons. The foot and mantle are striking: dark green mottlings on a rich cream background. The mantle of this snail can cover the outer surface of the shell almost completely. It is at this time, when the mantle is fully expanded, that it produces the spur on the apex of the shell. The spur may be an inch long. In the bottom figure the foot, mantle, up-turned siphon, head with eyes and tentacles are easily distinguished. This species is found in deep water (about 150–200 feet) on mud, or sand and mud bottoms from around Rio de Janeiro, Brazil, south to the Golfo San Matias, Argentina.

Bivalves can be found in freshwater, but not on land. Scientists group all bivalves together in another *class*, because they are basically alike.

So many bivalves are good to eat that we are familiar with many kinds: oysters, scallops, clams, cockles and mussels. Furthermore, there are several varieties of each of these kinds.

Bivalves are often spoken of as "the clams," but it is confusing to call an oyster or a mussel a "clam," especially if this name brings to mind a particular kind of bivalve which you know as this or that clam. For example, there are the littleneck clams, cherrystone clams, marsh clams, cleft clams, coral-boring clams, and all sorts of nut clams and bitter-sweet clams.

It is more sensible, and much more scientific, to start out calling all the hinged shells of two parts *bivalves*. In talking about a shell it is more important to be exact about its class than to know the name of that particular one, or its family name.

There are six classes of mollusks. Each class is made up of shells that are alike in important ways and different from the shells in the other classes. It is important to know the scientific names of the classes because they appear in the books you will have to use to identify your shells. The names may appear difficult at first glance but are not hard to pronounce when divided into syllables.

GAS-TROP'O-DA (găs-trŏp'ô-dà).

This is the largest class. An individual in this class is frequently called a gas'tro-pod (găs'trô-pŏd). This is the third name by which a spiral shell of one piece—a snail or univalve—may be called. There are roughly eighty thousand species of gastropods, and about half of these live in the sea.

The usual form of a gastropod shell is a spiral. The young of some species start off with a twist but mature in an untwisted shape. Others cover up the early spirals. Keyhole limpets, *Fissurella* (fĭs'ŭ-rĕl'à) and cowries, *Cypraea* (sī-prē'à) are examples.

Each complete turn of a snail shell is called a *whorl*. The last, and largest, is called the *body whorl*. All the whorls above the *body whorl* make up the *spire*. The tiptop of the spire is the *apex*. The opening, wherever it is located, is called the *aperture*.

Most snails creep along on a pad-like foot which expands .and contracts, pulling the shell along. There are, however, interesting variations to fit a particular kind of snail to a special environment. Many species have a horny or calcareous plate, the *operculum* (ô-pûr'kŭ-lŭm), meaning a lid or cover, attached on top of the foot and to the rear. This "trapdoor" may close the aperture snugly when the snail withdraws completely into the shell, sealing in moisture enough to last the animal some time; and sealing out some enemies. The *operculum* of some species, however, is very small or slender and does not close the aperture.

13

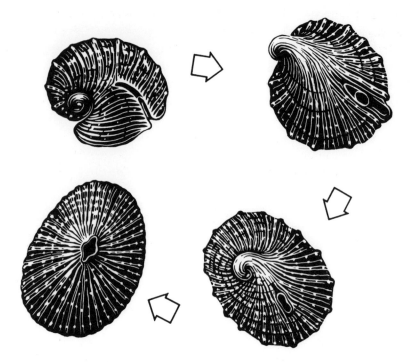

Growth stages of a keyhole limpet, Fissurella. *Greatly magnified. The first three stages show the snail's spiral form; and the slit of the lip becoming a hole moving toward the top. In the mature specimen (lower left, about life-size) all trace of the spiral form has disappeared. The organs, however, are twisted or curled so that the mouth and anus are not far apart.*

Some snails have a fleshy siphon through which water is drawn in. In many species there is a prominent shelly trough or *canal* which serves as a protective cover for the siphon. The *siphonal canal* may be curved or straight, short or long. In many shells there is just a groove or notch for the up-lifted siphon.

There is a "head" with tentacles and sometimes eyes which are far from keen. The eyes may be mere dots at the side or base of the tentacles; or quite large and at the end of a stalk. The mouth is sometimes just under the head; sometimes at the end of a long snout called the *proboscis* (prŏ-bŏs′ĭs).

The tongue-like organ enabling snails (and some of the other mollusks) to obtain food, is called the *radula* (răd′ū-là). This long, ribbon-like membrane is set with many tiny, tough teeth, and is fastened to the base of an inner mouth. The *radula* can be worked

14

back and forth to rasp and tear flesh for the flesh-eaters, or to scrape up vegetable matter for those preferring this diet.

It is fascinating to watch a snail using its toothy "tongue," and not difficult with large species having a snout. Experimenters placed a piece of raw fish in the end of a six-inch test tube and waited to see what would happen. The snail grasped the tube in its foot and thrust its head into the open end of the tube only to find it was not near the nice-smelling fish. The watchers saw the wormlike snout emerge from under the head and stretch until it reached the fish. It was transparent enough for the observers to see the radula begin working back and forth as it sawed off bits of fish which were drawn inside for digestion.

Melongena corona feeding on a piece of fish at the bottom of a six-inch test tube. In Fig. 1, the head may be seen inside the test tube with the proboscis (snout) fully extended to reach the fish. In Fig. 2, the Melongena having rasped the food has pulled a piece part way up the tube for easier feeding. The ability to extend the snout so greatly shows graphically how these snails can feed on deeply buried bivalves.

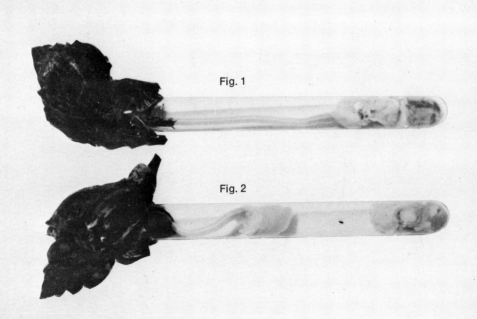

BI-VAL-VI-A (bī-văl'vǐ-à).

This is the next largest class. Formerly it was called PEL-E-CYP'O-DA (pĕl-ė-sǐp-ō-dà). An individual in this class is called a bivalve. There are about ten thousand species of bivalves, and most of these live in the sea. Many beautiful bivalves are found in freshwater, and among them are the famed pearl-producers in some rivers.

Some bivalves can only inch along on their one, wedge-like foot. This muscular foot cuts through the sand or mud, swells up or spreads out at the tip, and becomes rigid so that it serves as an anchor and the shell can be pulled along or down. In contrast to the slow-motion species, others can leap or burrow with agility to escape enemies. Some bivalves bore into wood or rock; and some, after a free-swimming period in youth, cement themselves on rocks, wrecks or other shells. Other bivalves anchor themselves to the bottom, to pilings, or to piers, with guy wires called the *byssus* (bǐs'ŭs). A few bivalves, the scallops and some related species, are able to "swim." They dart about in zigzags, snapping the valves together like castanets.

The fleshy mantle of a bivalve lines the two halves and sometimes extends in a beautiful fringe beyond the rim of the shells. Some mantles are brightly colored. The line that you saw running from "scar" to "scar" on some of your beach shells marks the place where the mantle was attached to the shell.

Scallops are noted for the glittery blue-green eyes that dot the mantle fringe close to the fluted rim of the shells. These bivalves not only have eyes but have good ones. Most bivalves are blind.

Bivalves live on tiny food particles in water which they draw in and expel through gaps in the mantle or a pair of tubes (siphons) which can extend beyond the mantle. Sometimes the siphons are enclosed in a casing, sometime not. Some can be drawn completely inside the shells when they are closed. The indentations you noticed in the line connecting the "scars" show where the siphons lay when withdrawn, even though they may be extended many times the depth of the indentation. The indentation is called the *pallial sinus*. A deep one usually shows that the bivalve can burrow deeply.

The "scars" are the places where the powerful *adductor* muscles were attached. Some species have one centrally located muscle, others have two muscles. The muscles are very powerful and, when contracted, can hold the shells shut for a long time. The large muscle is the part of a scallop that we eat. In France other parts of the scallop are eaten as well as the tender muscle.

The brittle "scab" which you noticed on some of the hinged shells is called the *ligament*. This horny band binds the two halves of the shell together. In some species it is on the outside, on others it is partly inside, and with others it is entirely inside. The internal springy arc seen in some bivalves is considered a part of the ligament. It is called the *resilium*. Some species have both the ligament proper and a resilium; some have one or the other. When the adductor muscle relaxes, these parts of the hinge pull and push the shells open.

The other four classes of mollusks will be discussed in another chapter. If you are interested in knowing the meaning of the class names, you can find five of them in a good dictionary or a shell book for more advanced collectors. The sixth class was added so recently that it is not listed in many handbooks or dictionaries.

No. 4

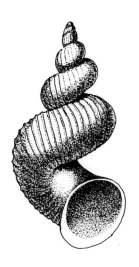

Chapter 5
Shell Names

Latin names seem to terrify most beginners. But if you want to be a shell collector, be a good one, and that means starting right off with the right names—the scientific ones. Nicknames are pretty and often descriptive, but very confusing. If you want to trade shells with other collectors, or buy them, you *have* to know the Latin names. The nickname you use may not be known to the collector with whom you want to trade; and commercial dealers use nothing but Latin names in listing their wares.

You can learn scores of names quickly by getting a field guide, studying the names and illustrations, then covering the names and asking yourself, "What is this?" Try only a few at a time and keep a score.

Don't worry about pronunciation at first. Do the best you can. Even if the accents aren't always on the right syllables, you are on the right track. Later you can look up the names. Almost without exception, the first half of a name (generic) can be found in any good dictionary, the syllables helpfully divided and accented; and frequently the second half (specific name) can be found, or at least the root from which it is derived.

Polishing pronunciation can come at any time; the significance of the game played early in one's collecting career is that it dispels all fear of scientific names, which frequently so paralyzes beginners that they won't even attempt to learn the names.

Many scientific names are no harder to say or to remember than the common ones. For example, it is just as easy to say *Pecten* as scallop; *Cardium* as cockle. If you look them up, you will find that these names came from Latin and Greek words meaning "comb" and "heart," or heart-shaped. With its fanning ribs, a single valve of any *Pecten* looks much like a Spanish comb; and, viewed from the side where the rims meet, most *Cardium* shells, and many kindred species,

look like valentine hearts. Learn these two now. *Pĕc′tĕn; Căr′dĭ-ŭm,*
Simple, isn't it?

Here are other easy-to-pronounce first names:

Trochus, Turbo, Oliva, Conus, Voluta, for: top, turban, olive,
cone, and volute shells. A volute is a spiral or scroll-like form.

Try this one: *Cyphoma,* cy-pho-ma. The *cy* is like the *cy* in *cy*cles;
the *pho* like those letters in *pho*tograph; and *ma,* in this case, rhymes
with "Ha!" The dictionary will give it: sī-fō′mȧ. It could be written:
sigh-foe′ mah. It means: humpbacked.

Some names can't be translated because they don't mean anything.
They were made up by the scientist who named the shell because
they had a nice sound. *Macoma* is one; *Livona* another. One book
lists ten species of *Macoma.* The common name for *Macoma tenta*
is Tenta Macoma! Is that any easier than the Latin name? The
person who made up the common name would have done better to
have called this shell the Stretched-out Macoma, because *tenta* comes
from a Latin word meaning stretched-out, elongated, as this bivalve is.

When scientific names have only a few syllables like the examples
given, it really is just as easy to learn them as the common names.
Many of us, however, are tempted to shy away from "long" or "big"
words with many syllables. But they, too, can be easy if you look
for clues and cut the words into manageable parts.

On our coasts there are several beautiful bivalves with the name
Trachycardium. At the first glance that looks very hard, doesn't
it? Take another look and you'll find part of that name is familiar:
car′di-um, heart-like. The first part, call it *"tray′ki"* or *"track′i"* (at
this point it does not matter about the exact pronunciation of the
a), put the two parts together, and you have: *tray′kĭ-car′dĭ-ŭm.*
That is no harder than Ethiopia or Abyssinia. If you look up *Trachy*
you will find you may pronounce it either "tray′ki" or "track′i"; and
the meaning is: rough. Some species of the heart-shaped bivalves
are smooth as eggs, but those with the prefix *Trachy-* are very rough.
Not only do they all have well-defined ribs, but the ribs are set with
sharp flanges.

If you can say *cardium,* it is child's play to manage the first part,
Trachy, especially when you know the meaning.

Another group of heart-sharped bivalves has the prefix *Dino-:*
Dinocardium. Suppose you look up *Dino* for yourself.

In the great family to which the beautiful *Pecten* shells belong,
Pectinidae, there are other groups, slightly different from the *Pecten*

19

group called *Placo-pecten, Lyro-pecten, Aequi-pecten*. In field guides these names are not hyphenated. Hyphens are used here just to prove that long names are not necessarily "hard."

So much for the first, or *generic*, name. What of the second, or *specific*, name? Many of these are easy to guess because they have been suggested by some feature of that particular shell—its color, shape, or structure; and sound like words we use often. Guess at the meaning and then look up: *carnea, rosea, citrina.* Try *ponderosa, ovalis, obesa, gibbus,* and *gibbosum;* then: *imbricatus, serrata, crenulata.* The endings won't be the same in English, but you will understand the meaning.

You will find many names ending in *i*. If you cover the letter with your finger, you will find names like *stearns, clark, hinds, austin.* If you put a capital letter in front of each you have: Stearns, Clark, Hinds, Austin—the names of people. The *i* ending shows that the people for whom the shells were named were all men. An *ae* ending shows that a woman was honored: *adelae* and *carolae* are examples.

Sometimes the people for whom shells were named were not friends, fellow-scientists, wives, or sweethearts of namers, but mythological beings. Two beautiful marine snails used the world over as trumpets are called *Charonia* (ká-rō′nǐ-á). The Atlantic species is *Charonia variegata;* the Pacific species is *Charonia tritonis* (see page 137). You can guess the meanings of *variegata* and *tritonis*. Who knows who Charon (kā′rŏn) was? Look the name up in a dictionary or an encyclopedia.

In English you are used to ignoring some letters in pronouncing some words; for example, the *g* in "gnat" and "gnaw." You will find this true in some words used for shell names, like *Chlamys*, for a group of bivalves closely kin to the *Pecten* group. In this word you ignore the *h*. The name is pronounced klā′mǐs or klăm′ǐs; and it means: a short cloak fastened at one place—just like the mantle of the bivalve. You will want to remember this name because some of the most brilliantly colored bivalves in the world are *Chlamys* this or that. They are handsome additions to a collection.

Start using a dictionary with the field guide you use for identifying your shells. Learning what the name means is interesting and helps you to remember it. Seeing how it is pronounced encourages you to try using the name. If you own the field guide, print the name as it should be pronounced beside the name in the book. If the book

20

is not yours, print the proper pronunciation under the name on the label you store with each specimen.

If you form the habit of looking up and jotting down, you will find that Latin names are simply not the bugaboos most amateurs allow them to be.

No. 5

Chapter 6
The Other Four Classes

Among the shells you picked up there may have been two so different from the spirally coiled univalves and the hinged bivalves that you set them aside from the others.

One of these is chalky white and coiled in a flat spiral but so loosely that the sides do not touch. The diameter of the coil is about one inch. The shell is pointed at the beginning of the spiral and open at the other end. If straightened out it would be a long, slender cone. The shell is so thin that you can see that the cone is divided into compartments. Among the broken snail shells you examined there was not one like this.

If the flatly coiled shell reminds you of a ram's horn, the other shell will remind you of an elephant's tusk. Unlike the tusk, however, it is open at both ends. It is about as big around as a pencil lead and not quite two inches long.

You were right in thinking these shells did not belong with the univalves and bivalves. They represent two other classes of mollusks.

The "ram's horn" belongs to this class.

CEPH-A-LOP'O-DA (sĕf-á-lŏp'ŏ-dá).

Individuals are called cephalopods (sĕf'á-lŏ-pŏds). These are the most highly developed mollusks and the class is filled with exceptions. Some members have an outside or *external* shell to which the fleshy part is attached. Some have an external shell to which it is not attached. Others have an *internal* shell which stiffens the soft body; and some have no shell at all.

With or without shells, all members of this class have tentacles around the mouth. Some have only eight, the shell-less octopuses, for example. Some have ten, and some have as many as ninety-four! The tentacles of some members have suckers, others do not.

The only cephalopods with a true shell are those belonging to the group (genus) called *Nautilus*. These shells are of one cone-shaped piece which is spirally coiled, but not like the univalves. *Nautilus* shells are flatly coiled so that both sides look exactly alike when the shell is sliced in half. Another difference is that they are divided into compartments like the "ram's horn" shell. These spaces are called *chambers*. A hollow tube connects all the chambers of a *Nautilus* shell. As the mollusk grows, it seals off the old chamber with a wall and lives in the new one. The male *Nautilus* has about sixty suckerless tentacles, and the female ninety-four (see page 28).

There are few living species of nautiluses. All of them are found in the Indian Ocean or the western part of the Pacific, and all are popularly called Chambered Nautilus. The scientific name for the most familiar species is *Nautilus pompilius* (pŏm-pĭl'ĭ-ŭs). The outside of the shell is creamy white streaked with wavy brown lines. The inside is lined with mother-of-pearl. In his famous poem about this shell, Oliver Wendell Holmes calls it "the ship of pearl" because he thought of it as "sailing" on the surface of the sea. Other members of this class do float at the surface, but the nautiluses live at great depths. Frequently they are caught in fish or crab traps.

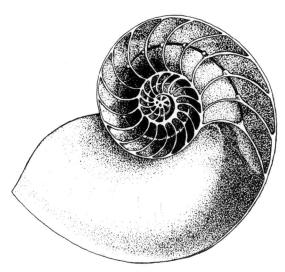

Nautilus pompilius—*Chambered Nautilus. Sectioned shell showing siphuncle (tube) connecting the chambers.*

Unless you are a world traveler, you probably will not be able to find a *Nautilus* shell yourself, but with luck you might find one of the beautiful shells of another kind of cephalopod called *Argonauta* (är-gō-nō′tà). There are several species of argonauts found in warm seas all around the world. The shells are so fragile, however, that it is rare to find a perfect specimen on the beach.

Because these shells are crinkled and paper-thin, they are popularly called "paper nautiluses" of one kind or another: Common Paper Nautilus, Brown Paper Nautilus, Knobby Paper Nautilus, and so forth. This is most confusing.

The octopus-like creatures which make these shells do not belong to the *Nautilus* group. The shells of the nautiluses and argonauts are coiled in the same way, but there the resmblance stops. There are no chambers in argonaut shells, and the shells are not attached to the body of the octopus-like animal. They are not true shells. They are not made primarily to protect the soft body, but as a container for the eggs of the female. The male argonaut is much smaller than the female and has no shell. Like octopuses, argonauts have only eight tentacles, whereas nautiluses have many. The argonaut's tentacles are studded with suckers as are those of octopuses.

Since argonauts are found in warm waters all around the world, a good many people have seen them alive at sea or stranded on the shore. Bit by bit the mystery of the argonaut's life history is being solved. It is so interesting that it deserves to be told in detail in another chapter.

The pretty little flatly coiled shell looking somewhat like a ram's horn is an example of an internal shell. Its chambers are connected by a tube like those of nautiluses. The name of the mollusk which makes this kind of shell to stiffen its body is *Spirula spirula* (spĭr′ŏŏ-là spĭr′ŏŏ-là). The shell is at one end of the bullet-shaped body and almost enclosed in it. A small portion of the shell shows from above and below. At the opposite end there are a pair of eyes and the mouth surrounded by tentacles, ten of them. This cephalopod lives deep in the ocean but comes up higher at night to feed, and may be caught in the tow nets of scientists. There is little chance of the average collector seeing one alive, but the pretty shell is a rather common find on beaches around the world. (See page 25).

The internal shell or "pen" of cephalopods we call squids and cuttlefishes may be thin and horny, or hard and shell-like. The "pen" of the common cuttlefish of Europe, *Sepia,* is about six inches long,

Spirula spirula—*"Ram's Horns." The gas-filled chambers of the* Spirula *keep this cephalopod afloat—the rear end, with the enclosed shell up; the tentacles dangling. When the animal dies, the shell floats to the surface where it drifts with winds and currents. European collectors call them "little post horns" because of their resemblance to the horns announcing the arrival of coaches in which people traveled.*

round at one end, pointed at the other, and made of a chalky substance. This is the familiar cuttlefish "bone" put in birdcages to provide lime. This mollusk ejects a black fluid as a protective "smoke" screen from enemies.

SCA-PHOP'O-DA (scă-fŏp'ŏ-dà).

The so-called "tusk" or "tooth" shells belong to this class. The popular names were suggested by the shape. Most of the two hundred living species and three hundred fossil species belong to the genus (group) called *Dentalium* (dĕn-tā'lĭ-ŭm). If you look up the name you will find it comes from the Latin words *dens* and *dentis* meaning: tooth. Some scaphopods (scăf'-ŏ-pŏds) are smooth, others are ridged lengthwise.

These mollusks are able to burrow into the sea bottom. The foot is a wormlike, muscular organ which can be expanded at the tip. Tentacle-like filaments surround the mouth and catch microscopic organisms for food. Foot and mouth are at the large end. The small end projects a little above the bottom surface.

The specimens washed on our beaches or dredged offshore are not larger around than pencil leads and rarely over two inches long.

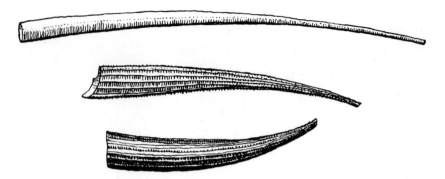

Scaphopods –*Tusk shells. Top:* Dentalium perlongum–*Very Long Tooth Shell. Middle:* Dentalium carduus–*Thistle Tooth Shell. Bottom:* Dentalium ceratum –*Wax-colored Tooth Shell.*

Larger and handsomer species are found in the Adriatic and Mediterranean Seas and in the Pacific around the Philippines. A fossil species found in Texas is ten inches long and more than an inch in diameter at the large end.

AM-PHI-NEU-RA (ăm-fĭ-nū′rà).

This mollusk class is made up of animals protected by a "coat-of-mail"—eight overlapping *valves* or *plates* of shell held together by a leathery *girdle* which may be quite pretty. Some girdles are covered with scales and look like patterned snakeskins. Others are covered with hair-like processes or tufts of bristle. Individuals in this class are called chitons (kī′tŏns).

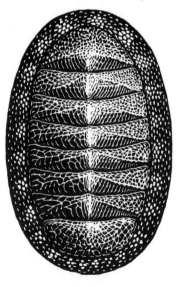

Top view of a chiton showing the eight plates and the encircling girdle.

The foot of a *chiton* is a muscular pad on which it can creep about or cling fast to its preferred living place under rocks along the shore, on rocks splashed with spray, or in very deep water. A tiny species often attaches itself to other kinds of mollusks.

Chitons are, basically, bilaterally symmetrical, that is: alike on both sides. Some organs, like nerves and gills, are paired and arranged serially. The mouth and anus are at opposite ends of the eight plates. For years chitons were classed as the most primitive mollusks. Now another class has taken this place.

MONO-PLA-COPH'O-RA (mŏnō-plă-cŏf'ŏ-rà).

Separated into syllables, the long name of this new class is not difficult.

Until 1957 only five classes of mollusks were recognized. In that year a scientist published a paper on a new kind of mollusk dredged from one of the ocean trenches off the west coast of Costa Rica by the Danish exploratory vessel *Galathea*. Ten living specimens and two shells were brought up. Later more specimens of a similar kind were dredged off the coast of Peru by the *Vema*, an exploratory vessel of Columbia University.

The shell of the new species is shaped like a back-pointed cap, oval, fragile, and almost transparent (see below). The underside is coated with mother-of-pearl. It looks quite like a true limpet and some other snails with pointed, cap-like shells. A look at the underside and careful dissection, showed the mollusk was no snail.

Neopilina galatheae—*Galathea's New Pilina*. Right: Looking down on the limpet-like shell. Left: Underside of a living specimen showing the chiton-like, bilateral symmetry: mouth (top) and anus (bottom) opposite each other; the foot (light center) and five pairs of flat finger-like filaments just inside the mantle edge (dark area around the foot).

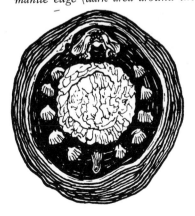

There is a pad-like foot in the center (see page 27) and a mantle; but the mouth (top) and the anus (bottom) are opposite each other as they are in chitons. Furthermore, arranged around the mantle in pairs are five short stems with flat, fleshy filaments rather like leaves on a stem. The scientific name for such a structure is *cte-nid'i-um* (tĕ-nĭd'i-ŭm) (gill); the *c* is silent. Dissection showed several paired organs, among which were eight pairs of strong muscles. These paired organs are very chiton-like.

Scientists who were familiar with fossil shells saw right away that the newly dredged shells were like a type, or class, of fossil shells called *Pilina* which had eight paired muscle scars. The fossil shells had lived three hundred and fifty million years ago. Scientists thought that all mollusks of this class had died out. Now here was a species closely related to the fossil species which had survived in the deeper parts of the sea.

The newly discovered mollusk was named *Neopilina*, meaning "new Pilina." The second part of the name honors the Danish vessel which dredged the first prize specimens: *galatheae*. It is pronounced găl-à-thē'ē. The whole name is *Neopilina galatheae*.

Since the new mollusk could not be classified with the gastropods (snails) because the organs were so different or with the chitons because it had only a single shell, the ancient fossil class was instituted to contain both the living species and the fossils which resemble each other so closely.

Thus a sixth class took its place with the well-known five. The name of this class means "having one plate," to distinguish these mollusks from the eight-plated chitons.

No. 6

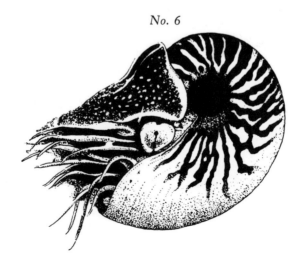

Chapter 7
How to Comb a Beach

Suddenly you realize the shells you picked up are not as pretty as they seemed at first. The colors have faded; the gloss is gone. Other beachcombers have been disappointed with their first finds too. It happened to the poet Ralph Waldo Emerson, who described his shells as "poor, unsightly, noisome things," that "left their beauty by the shore, with the sun and the wind and the wild uproar." Gleaming from the last wave, foam-flecked, sand-frosted, his shells, like yours, had been breathtakingly beautiful. Foam and frosting were seaside disguises. Unmasked the shells are unlovely. The sun and sand have faded their colors and dulled their sheen.

Beginner's luck for shell collectors is usually bad luck because beginners don't know how to look for shells that will hold their beauty as long as they are cared for.

While you were grabbing up bright, shining shells, the veteran collectors were walking slowly behind:

— Looking under dead and dying mounds of seaweed.
— Breaking open sponges.
— Turning over barnacled planks.
— Examining big, old broken shells.
— Emptying cans and bottles.
— Peering into rusty drums or buoys.
— Pulling streamers of green "moss" floating like mermaids' hair in tide pools.
— Tracing tunnels like mole-runs in wet sand.
— Prodding blobs of "jelly" or soft flesh.
— Pocketing shells covered with "soot" or dry bristles.

They were looking for and finding living mollusks. Learn from the veterans. It pays to make haste slowly in beach collecting. Pass up the shells that look prettiest. Those that seem ugly will turn out to be the prettiest. When properly cleaned and stored they will retain their color and gloss indefinitely. Learn to look in, on and under the objects where mollusks took refuge in the sea; learn to read the shoreline signs that point to hidden shells.

Beach drift may not only hide prizes from the hurriers looking for something pretty in full view, but it may protect fragile shells from heavy heels and hungry sea birds. Its dampness may also keep delicate mollusks alive for some time. Damp or dry, it is well to look under, and through sea wrack. Try shaking dry wrack over a dark cloth. You may find dozens of miniature shells so small, or near sand color, that they might never be seen on a well-trodden beach.

This is a good way to find the beautifully sculptured, snow-white wentletraps, *Epitonium* (ĕp-ĭ-tō′nĭ-ŭm), and related species with other names. The popular name for this genus (a group of species) comes from a Danish word meaning "winding staircase," so amateurs often call them staircase shells. There are many species found in shallow and deep water of our coasts, and all are beautiful.

California collectors search the yellowing kelp thrown on their beaches, for the thin, translucent apricot or brown scallops, *Leptopecten* (Lepto-pecten) *latiauratus* (la-ti-au-ra′tus), which are often found alive fastened to the holdfasts. These shells may also be

Epitonium humphreysi (Humphrey's Wentletrap or Staircase Shell) and necklace-like string of egg clusters. Greatly enlarged. This species is typical of the Carolinian Province. This specimen was collected alive in a sheltered sound and laid the eggs in an aquarium. Each "bead" in the string is a mixture of eggs and grains of sand held together by a gluey secretion.

found attached to stones and to the bottoms of boats; but, because they are so often on kelp, they are often commonly called Kelp-weed Scallops.

Break open sponges. Bivalves which have passed the free-swimming stages of their life cycles may have attached themselves by the byssus to, or in, sponge.

A plank covered with barnacles and mud may have choice bivalves attached to it. A wing shell or "oyster," would be a likely find in the warm water zone of either the Atlantic or Pacific coast of North America. The Latin name *Pteria* (the *p* is silent) means "wing." Both *Pteria colymbus* (kŏ-lim'bus), the Atlantic species, and *Pteria sterna,* the Pacific species, have a wing-like extension at the hinge-line. Both species are dark—black, brown, or purplish, on the outside; and covered with a fine periostracum. Inside they are lined with lavender-blue mother-of-pearl. The Pacific species, like the "pearl oyster," *Pinctada mazatlanica* (Mazatlan Pearl Shell) of that coast, was fished so extensively for pearls after the coming of the Spaniards that both species were nearly exterminated. Richer beds lured the pearlers away and saved these beautiful bivalves from extinction. Anchored to a mud bottom, they are found in shallow water offshore and are rated as common or fairly so.

Like planks, large, dead shells may have a variety of small, living mollusks clinging to them, or growing on them: a limpet, slipper-shell, chiton, or a tiny jewel box, *Chama* (kā'mà).

Delicate, tiny oyster drills, *Eupleura,* have been found in long-drowned bottles.

A tide pool may seem empty except for what beginners would describe as green "moss," floating like mermaids' hair. Try pulling several strands. You might find only a broken bivalve dangling from the end; but you could find a lively snail which had burrowed into the sand looking for a live bivalve to dine on.

Prod with a stick, for safety, any jelly-like or fleshy object on the beach. It could be any one of a dozen creatures that you'd not want and which might make your fingers itch or sting; but it could be a mollusk you'd like very much for your collection—perhaps one of the pretty little "lady's ear" or "baby's ear" shells (*Sīn'ŭm*) which are completely enveloped by the fleshy parts. The most common species of the Atlantic and Gulf coasts looks like a cream-colored oyster and the ear-shaped shell is white. A rare Pacific coast species with a purplish-brown shell, has mahogany-colored soft parts.

31

Trace sandy tunnels like mole-runs. Buried at the end you may find one of the many "moon" shells or "shark eyes" called *Lunatia* (from luna, moon), *Polinices* (pŏl-ĭ-nī´sēz), or *Natica* (năt´ĭ-kà). The name *Polinices,* loosely translated means "a victor," or "one of many victories." All of these closely related globe-shaped snails prey on other mollusks (see page 128). Some tunnels lead you to big or little olive shells: *Oliva* and *Olivella.*

Two collectors vacationing on the west coast of Mexico went beachcombing before unpacking their bags. One of them wrote me: "Right in front of *the* hotel, the only one on the coast, we saw a dimple in the sand as a wave receded. I dug with my finger and up came a pretty little snail I had never seen before. We could not find it in any of our books. Dr. X. at the university kindly identified it for us. It is *Cominella subrostratus,* fairly common right here, but rare everywhere else. If we return we will try to get a specimen for the university collection."

Beachcombing is a back-breaking business. Save yourself useless bends by rolling over any doubtful shells with your toe or a stick. A dingy or dirty-looking shell is worth an immediate bend. These are the freshest shells still coated with the protective periostracum which may look like soot, fuzz, wet fur or matted hair. Often such shells are still alive. With recently dead snails, the operculum, when the species has one, may still be attached to the foot.

In years to come, when your collection has grown, you may weed out all the beachworn shells; but any you found with the periostracum and the operculum will always have a place in your collection—or in your box of duplicates for exchanging with other collectors.

Beachcombing sometimes rewards the collector with a rare sight which a serious amateur may value as much as finding a fine or rare shell. Such experiences go into their logs or letters.

A Florida collector wrote me: "One Sunday in February I went with a group of friends to a party on Key Largo. Our hostess lived in a cottage on the inner side. As I was the only sheller in the group I had not gone prepared to do any collecting, but could not resist a walk on the beach. Imagine my surprise to see Keyhole Limpets crawling along in the sand! Many of them. It is the first time I've ever seen a limpet that was not clinging fast to a rock. I had no idea they ever left their rocks."

An Australian friend wrote that, beachcombing around Roebuck

Bay on the west coast, she and her husband came to a sandbar and there "found dozens of *Cypraea walkeri* (Walker's Cowry), crawling boldly around in the bare sand. Very odd behavior for any *Cypraea,* and the reason for it beyond our understanding."

As you walk the beach, watch for unusual sights; and pause to watch the behavior of the mollusks you are lucky enough to find alive.

No. 7

Chapter 8
High Winds
and Hurricanes

Some beaches offer good collecting most of the time because they are in tropical or semi-tropical zones whose warm waters support a large and varied mollusk population; and also because they are protected in some way from the fury of the open sea, so that the shells brought ashore on high tides after high winds are not broken badly or at all.

High winds and hurricanes can transform the unprotected beaches of "open coasts" into happier hunting grounds. No one in his right mind would rush to the shore during a hurricane; but there is no reason not to be on hand in a high wind, especially a steady one. At such times beauties from the high seas are often blown ashore unharmed.

Even though many of the shells hurled ashore in a hurricane may be damaged, others will survive the rough treatment. The beach will be piled with flotsam and jetsam, all sorts of wreckage from far out and deep down. In or on any of these objects, as you have seen, there may be wonderful shells securely anchored by their own devices.

Our "open" north Gulf coast offers beautiful bathing beaches and excellent fishing, but very little beach collecting except after storms. Two collectors on this shore had the luck to find a rusty oil drum after a hurricane. Inside there were two small, living *Murex* shells with such delicate spines that the collectors did not recognize them at first as juveniles of the fairly common, rugged Great Eastern Murex (*Murex fulvescens*) of this coast. Even though the shells were not rarities, they were in perfect condition; and finding them on this coast was a rare experience.

Other collectors found part of an ocean buoy, clean on the outside from the yearly scraping and painting, but heavily encrusted inside with a variety of marine organisms. The prizes in the buoy were several Leafy Jewel Boxes (*Chama macerophylla*) (facing page 36), some lemon yellow, some white, in perfect condition; at least the top valve of each specimen was covered with flawless "ruffles." The bottom valves were flat, or nearly so, and attached so firmly to the curved metal that they had to be removed with a chisel.

Such marine bivalves go through a short, free-swimming larval stage at the surface of the sea, before they settle and attach themselves to the solid objects which will be "home" from then on. No matter how many others settle in the same area, once attached there is no moving away. Lacking room to grow, many specimens under such crowded conditions are quite distorted. These animals live on microscopic organisms strained from the water which is circulated through the mantle cavity by the action of cilia, hair-like processes.

Specimens attached to concrete bases to which buoys are anchored, like those on rocks, are often broken and blunted by the scouring action of sand swirling in stormy water; or are heavily coated with marl, which hardens like concrete; or are encrusted by other marine growths. Inside the buoys, however, the same species are protected. They are not buffeted by agitated water, yet there is enough movement to bring a steady supply of food and oxygen. Since it is dark, the encrusting growths which must have sunlight do not cover these specimens. Every spine or foliation develops in delicate perfection, unless the shell is crowded too closely by its neighbors.

Our best finds on the Alabama coast after a hurricane were seven turret-shaped snails belonging to the family Epitoniidae (wentletraps or staircase shells): *Amaea mitchelli*, Mitchell's Amaea. *Amaea* is another of the made-up names which baffle translators. Beachcombers in jeeps were thoughtlessly racing along the firm sand looking for whatever of interest might have been thrown ashore: glass balls used as fishnet floats in some countries, old bottles, big shells. My husband and I worked the line of black sea wrack, lifting it, shredding it, shaking it. Of the seven brown and white wentletraps we found, five were alive. These uncommon shells are washed up rather often on Texas beaches. Those we found were the first in our collection from Alabama (see page 162).

Good collecting is not ended with the storm. In the days following storms, high tides and less violent waves may wash ashore shells which have been gouged from the sand, or stripped from the protection of a reef, but not thrown ashore in the midst of the violence. Letters from two collectors in foreign lands tell of such incidents.

"I am enclosing a picture of the 'Glory-of-the Sea' (Conus gloria-maris) which was collected after two typhoons swept the Philippines in October, 1957, within ten days of each other. The first typhoon was most appropriately named Gloria! The Conus was found on the reef in the Vical region near Ragay Gulf, Southwestern Luzon, with the mollusk still fresh. It is four and three-quarter inches long, and perfect.

"In 1955, a juvenile specimen of about two and a half inches was found in Bohol, the same island where Hugh Cuming found the three matured specimens on the reef in 1838."

Finding these Conus shells supported the Philippine collector's belief that this species is not extinct in his homeland, and helped to dissipate a cherished myth. According to legend, the reef on which Cuming found three of these beautiful and rare cones sank into the sea soon after. Although its disappearance was not accompanied by the tolling of bells and chanting of dirges, like Debussy's enchanted cathedral, it has been mourned ever since by a multitude. Because with it, they believed, went the last of the Conus gloria-maris. No more were ever found, myth said, even though expeditions from many places in the world had been sent to search for them.

Malacologists smile at the legend, and count off on their fingers specimens, with reliable locality data, discovered since Cuming's time at other places in the Philippines and Dutch East Indies.

Even so, there have been so few specimens found since the first record was published in 1757, that when some are destroyed as they were in the war, or reported as "missing" from some collection, a first grader could do the subtraction.

Thus, one addition to the world's small hoard is news in the shell-collecting world, and the finder a very lucky person.

The other letter came from an Australian. Her find was a Great Spotted Cowry, Cypraea guttata (see page 134). "It is not a mature specimen, but it is perfect; and I collected it myself which, of course, makes it a top marker."

This is one of the rarest cowries. Most of the seventeen known specimens are in museum collections. This cowry is also one of the

Puperita pupa (Zebra Nerites) and *Tectarius muricatus* (Beaded Periwinkles). John Lewis Stage

Spondylus americana (Thorny Oyster) with *Chama macerophylla* (Yellow Jewel Box). John Lewis Stage

most beautiful. The base color ranges from yellow to reddish brown, liberally sprinkled with white dots of varying sizes. The teeth, which extend across the base and over the sides, are ridges of bright red. "I found it a day or so after a blow on a mainland beach. It was served up on a platter for me, so to speak, by the typhoon. This bit of luck is one of those things which happen once in a collector's lifetime."

The discovery of three beachcombers at Naples, Florida, is perhaps a more spectacular piece of hurricane luck than those of the Philippines and Australia. Three women who ran a shell shop decided to spend Thanksgiving Day beachcombing. They had not walked farther than the public beach, right at the end of a busy main street, when three pairs of eyes spotted the shell at the same moment and three heads bumped as backs bent and hands grabbed. "Ariel got there first," one of the others told the newspaper reporter, for of course the news got around in a hurry. The article appeared under this title: *"One in-a-Million" Shell Found.*

All three collectors recognized the shell immediately: a Juno's Volute, or *"junonia,"* from the Latin name *Scaphella junonia.* A few of these beautiful, deep-water snails—white, spotted evenly and profusely with chocolate-brown squares—wash ashore on the west coast of Florida yearly and are prize finds for beachcombers. This one, however, was a one-in-a-million find because it was a "left-turn" specimen.

The spiral of most snails turns like the hands of a clock, to the right, so that the opening, *aperture,* is on the right side when the shell is held with the spire up. Sometimes, however, a snail may spiral in the opposite direction, counter-clockwise. The aperture then is on the left. Such shells are called left-handed or left-turn shells by amateurs, and *sinistral* by scientists, which means the same thing.

This specimen was dead and flawed. It had a break in the body-whorl caused by some accident which the animal survived, because it continued to add to the shell beyond the broken place.

Neither its being dead nor damaged mattered to collectors, who knew how rarely a normally right-turn species takes the wrong turn; but to hear from Dr. Harald A. Rehder, Curator of Mollusks at the United States National Museum, that this was the first record of a left-handed *Scaphella junonia* he knew of, made the shell a priceless treasure: the-one-and-only, so far known.

On a beach after a storm, you can never tell what may lie just a few feet ahead. For this reason even veteran collectors may be found beachcombing. Generally, however, the veterans leave the beaches to the beginners. They search for shells beyond the beach for there they are more certain of finding good shells. Luck is involved, but it is more a matter of know-how.

No. 8

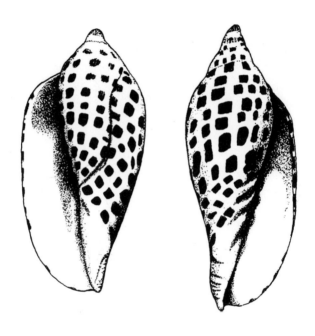

Chapter 9
How to
Pick a Good
Collecting Place

From seasoned collectors, beginners discover that the delight of finding what chance rolls at your feet cannot compare with the thrill of searching beyond the beach. From knee to neck-deep in the sea and as far beyond as you can safely dive with a face mask, there is far greater opportunity of finding perfect specimens. Furthermore, when you look for shells in the places they live (native habitats), collecting becomes "hunting."

Success demands more than energy and enthusiasm. It depends, as with every form of hunting, on the extent of one's knowledge and the degree of one's skill. There are many tricks to learn, techniques to master, and then—new shores to explore.

A prospective shell hunter must learn first how to pick a good collecting place. He must know what factors create favorable living conditions for mollusks, otherwise he may waste energy and hours— maybe a whole vacation—searching a barren shore.

In appraising a coast you must consider: the degree of wave shock; the type of bottom—rock, sand, mud, grass, dead and living coral, or combinations of these; and the tidal range.

Few mollusks can survive on coasts exposed to the violence of pounding surf. Those that do are especially adapted for life in this tumultuous environment. Therefore, forget the hard-packed beaches with the great rollers the surfers love. Occasionally you will find right at the shore colonies of little bivalves or small snails exposed by a receding wave. In a moment they have burrowed in the soft sand again. With luck and a face mask, out neck-deep on a calm day, you might find a colony of olive shells, *Oliva*, tunneling just under the surface of the sand. There are several hundred species of the colorful, glossy mollusks around the world. On exposed sandy coasts most mollusks live far beyond the low tide line where they are less likely to be scoured out of the sand by surging waves.

Four kinds of rock-clinging snails. There are many species of each of these kinds of snails. Top, left: A cup-and-saucer shell, Crucibulum. Top, right: An abalone or sea ear, Haliotis. Bottom, left: A "true" limpet, Acmaea. Bottom, right: A "keyhole" limpet, Diodora.

Forget also dramatic rock cliffs with battering breakers. Only a few hardy species of mollusks have been able to adapt to such a rugged environment. They cluster deep in crevices or plaster themselves to the rock to withstand the crash and suck of the surf. On calm days, if the rocks are not too steep or slippery for safety you can collect the species that thrive in this habitat around the world in both warm and cold seas.

Look instead for coasts protected from the fury of the waves by twin promontories, like encircling arms; a bold headland; a long peninsula; or offshore islands. Submerged reefs, rocks, or bars break the force of the waves. Even submarine "forests" of seaweed called kelp serve as such a protective barrier that ships on the American west coast have taken refuge back of them in stormy weather. The force of the surf is also broken by a gradually shelving slope.

The famed beaches of Florida's west coast are protected by a gentle slope and offshore reefs. In southern California, giant, fern-like kelps protect the shore. These seaweeds may be more than one hundred and fifty feet long and only part of this length grows upright from the rocky bottom. The rest floats on the surface of the water forming a thick "canopy" which breaks the force of the waves.

Various types of bottom afford further protection for mollusks on sheltered coasts. Those that are best for shells and shellers are shunned by bathers: mud, firm or squishy; sand with meadows of seaweed, or strewn with rubble and loosely bedded rocks. On rocky coasts look for stretches with a broad shelf pitted with pockets, potholes, and tide pools tapestried with colorful algae. Here at low tide the hunting will be good. Search on and under the rocks and be prepared to look hard. The mollusks themselves may be cloaked with algae or camouflaged by bright mantles or shell patterns which blend with the algae.

On coasts with a great tidal range, acres of prime hunting ground are completely exposed or made accessible by low or "minus" tides. The tide cuts the shoreline into four distinct zones which are easily seen on rocky coasts. The zones are called: spray, high-tide, mid-tide, and low-tide.

The mollusks found in the spray zone are able to live without water for long periods. This part of the shore is touched only by spray and storm tides. Mollusks of the high-tide zone must also be able to stand long exposure to air because tides high enough to cover them do not occur often. The number of species which can live for so long without water is limited, but among them are some of the prettiest shells.

The food supply is obviously an important factor governing the number and kinds of animals which can live in a given area. The shifting population of the high-tide zones of some rocky shores are an interesting example. In such a place barnacles, limpets, and mussels often play a game of musical chairs, in which, to continue the figure of speech, carnivores from a lower zone call the tune.

The algae-covered rocks are grazing fields for the herbivorous limpets. Clamped firmly in their "home spots," often occupied for such lengths of time that they become pits, the limpets wait out the ebb of the tide, their gills bathed in water trapped beneath their shells. With the return of the tide they begin to roam over the rocks, scraping up food with their radulae, or many-toothed, ribbon-like tongues. Sometimes the competition is so keen that the rocks are literally licked clean, and the greedy, or too numerous, limpets must migrate to greener pastures. Quick to seize this opportunity, the mussels and barnacles vie with each other for space on the rocks; but in the struggle for existence, they have not long to enjoy their territorial expansion.

To the snails living at a lower level, the rocks are now spread with *their* kind of food and up they come to feast. If there are enough of them, they can finish off the colonies leaving the rocks covered with empty shells which sand-laden surf will eventually wear away.

Then once more the scoured rocks will become carpeted with algae and the limpets can return.

Under typical conditions the mid-tide zone is covered and uncovered daily by the tide or tides. On some coasts there are two high tides and two low tides each day. In this zone there is a great jump in the mollusk population. The species living in this zone are not only hardy enough to live through this constant change from wet to dry, but are so remarkably adapted that they take advantage of it, or actually require it to survive. The timing of the breeding period of a Pacific coast chiton is a good example of adaption to the conditions in the zone. Studies show that when the tide is out the water in rocky pools is quiet, an ideal time for the fertilization of the greatest number of eggs. And so at this time only does this all-important phase of the life cycle take place. At low tide in May and June, the males release their sperm in the placid basins. With all in readiness, the females begin to release their eggs and continue to lay until the first wave of the returning tide splashes into the pool. At this moment the egg-laying stops abruptly.

The most exciting area for the shell collector is the low-tide zone. It is thickly populated with mollusks and other animals. They are exposed only by the lowest tides.

Like monied men watching stock reports, keen collectors watch the tide tables for the few times each month or season they may expect low or extremely low tides. The extreme lows are called *minus* tides. At such times, and for just a few hours, normally inaccessible reefs, flats, and bars of the fourth tidal zone are bared. The species living in the low-tide zone are not as common in collections as those living closer in and so within easy reach most of the time.

With the falling tide, your quarry will have crept into or under whatever protective cover there is. Again you will have to look with sharp eyes.

Never forget that a rapidly falling tide will be matched by a swift rise. On coasts where the vertical range of the tide may be ten, twenty or even thirty feet, to be caught far out as the tide rushes in can be dangerous and might be fatal. Don't become so engrossed with your hunting that you forget to keep track of the time. A rule

Author collecting in a protected inlet at low tide.

of thumb is an hour for the fall and another for the rise. On coasts where there is real danger, check tide times and range with people who know the coast; or better, go out with a guide.

Malacologists divide the world into zones or "provinces" which are determined by the range of certain species. On the Pacific coast of North America there are: the Aleutian, Californian, and Panamic Provinces; on the Atlantic there are: the Boreal, Carolinian, and the Caribbean. The boundaries are not clear-cut; there is some overlapping. For laymen, the second and third provinces on the east and the west coasts offer the best collecting.

The Californian Province extends from the state of Washington to some way south of the border between California and Mexico on the Pacific coast. The Panamic, overlapping the Californian, starts around San Diego and continues to northern Ecuador. The Gulf of California is in this province.

On the Atlantic coast, the Carolinian Province extends from Cape

Cod to about St. Augustine, Florida. Then, beginning at Cape Sable, at the tip of Florida's west coast, it swings around the Gulf coast to near Vera Cruz, Mexico.

The Caribbean Province is roughly triangular, stretching from Bermuda west to Mexico near Tampico; swinging southeast around the coast of Central and South America to some way down the coast of Brazil; and then north to Bermuda, enclosing the Caribbean Islands, the Bahamas, and part of Florida's east coast.

The marine life of the Panamic and Caribbean Provinces is tropical and much alike because in ages past there was a natural Panama "canal," permitting free circulation between east and west seas. A later geological upheaval thrust up a narrow land-barrier between them. Both of these tropical Provinces offer fine collecting areas.

Our West Atlantic coral reefs are in the Caribbean Province. Although less well-known than the fabled reefs of the western Pacific, collecting on them is an exciting experience and can add many beautiful shells to a collection.

Atlantic reefs are terraced. The first terrace, or inner reef zone next to the land, is the best for shelling. The "forests" of stony corals which attract the underwater photographers are on the second terrace in deeper water. The inner zone is a rocky shoal with small "stony" corals, "soft" corals—sea fans and whips; hydroids and encrusting algae. These shoreline reefs are rarely exposed but at low or minus tides the water is shallow and clear enough for easy collecting.

The outer reefs well beyond the shore, and often linking a string of little islands, are dangerous except at dead low and in a dead calm. Only experienced collectors should attempt to "work" them. There should be a boat standing by, not just "due to return," in case of a sudden change in the weather which is normal in these waters.

Hawaii, our fiftieth state, falls just inside the eastern tip of the Indo-Pacific Province, the largest province of them all and the richest shelling area in the world (see pages 98-99).

The reefs around the Hawaiian Islands are more like those of the west Atlantic than the so-called "classic" reefs of the western Pacific. Hawaiian reefs are described as "weak," meaning the conditions are not right for luxuriant coral growth. The islands are surrounded with "platforms" or terraces of rubble, sand, some corals and seaweeds—with a fine assemblage of mollusks suited to this habitat.

Learn to read the Tide Tables and the charts published by the

United States Coast and Geodetic Survey and the hydrographic charts published under the supervision of the Navy. The Tide Tables are published yearly and cover both coasts of North and South America. The Tables and coastal charts may be obtained for moderate fees from the U. S. Department of Commerce, Coast and Geodetic Survey, Washington, D. C. 20401, and at many marine supply stores. Buy and study those for the islands or coastal areas that interest you as possible collecting spots.

No. 9

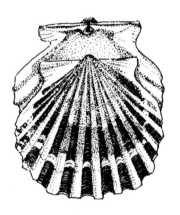

Chapter 10
Collecting Equipment

The kind of equipment you need will depend on the kind of place you plan to collect in and the depth of water.

In Shallow Water

In areas that are exposed or barely filmed with water at low tide, you need only minimum equipment: shoes of some kind, a collecting bag, and whatever protection you want from the sun and glare. Shoes are essential. Most collectors wear tennis shoes, but some prefer heavier ones on coral reefs or slippery rocks. Your game bag can be anything: a cloth bag, a plastic bucket, a picnic basket. Suit yourself about sun lotion, a shirt, hat, and dark glasses.

Water-Glass.

In water less than a foot deep, there may be times when you need a "water-glass," a wooden bucket or box with a glass bottom. Even in crystal-clear water, the slightest ripple may make it difficult to see the bottom; with a ruffled surface, flowing tide, swaying seaweeds, and dancing shadows, it is impossible. But through the glass bottom, resting on the surface of the water, you can see the world below clearly and in magnified detail.

Wooden buckets such as sponge fishermen use, available at marine supply houses, are ideal because of the large glass area, a foot or more in diameter. If you are close to your collecting spot, a sponger's bucket is fine. If, however, you must travel some distance in a well-packed car, or fly, it is a great convenience to have nesting boxes like those we use (see page 51). Ours are a help in another way: two pairs of wet sneakers fit in nicely.

The boxes are rectangular, and one is just enough smaller than the

The author's husband studying a coastal chart. Collecting bag in hand. Sponger's bucket at his feet.

other to fit into it neatly. Although the glass areas are small (5" x 13" and 4" x 11"), they are adequate.

Our boxes were made by attaching ¼-inch marine plywood sides to cypress ends; then inserting the glass bottoms between two sets of cypress strips or "stops." The glass is bedded in below-waterline seam compound; caulking compound or white lead would serve. Copper or brass fastenings should be used to prevent corrosion. To each of our boxes is affixed a combination handle and shoulder strap made of a one-inch wide cotton webbing army belt, more comfortable than the original rope handles.

Both boxes are painted dull black inside to cut down reflections on the glass. Keeping the inner surface of the glass wet improves the visibility. Sometimes the glass is helped by a treatment of spit and polish. I don't know what the magical property of saliva is, but it works wonders on glass buckets and face masks.

Although it gives you no more than a knothole view, in an emergency a face mask floated on the water serves as a substitute for a "water-glass." As long as you are collecting on foot, a water-glass is indispensable.

Gloves, Crowbars, Garden Forks.

Where there are rocks to be turned, gloves, a crowbar, or a garden fork with bent prongs are useful. Cotton "work" gloves are a protection against scratches, stings, bites, and broken fingernails. A large crowbar is necessary when collecting on foot at low tide where there are large rocks and coral heads to be turned. A smaller bar or hooked garden fork is sufficient for submerged rocks, and either of these is much easier to dive with in deeper water.

Screens and Sieves.

If you find small shells especially appealing—tiny species or juveniles of larger species, and many people do—then try your luck at "screening." This collecting method can be practiced by those born lazy as well as those with energy to squander.

If you are the take-it-easy type, buy a large kitchen sieve or colander and see what you can find by scooping up and sifting sand on the beach or from the shallows.

Or better, make a wood frame with a bottom of fine wire mesh; or a set of three frames superimposed, with wire mesh of graduated sizes. Such frames are often used by collectors who dredge, but can be used in the shallows where the collector with a strong back can dig up spadefuls of the bottom and sluice the sand or mud with buckets of water. Set up the screens as far out as low tide will permit.

ON ROCKY SHORES

On rocky shores you will need a scout knife and chisel, and sometimes a hammer, to dislodge cling-fast species like chitons, limpets, abalones, and some bivalves. A small-mesh dip net, or a kitchen sieve attached to a long handle, is helpful in scooping specimens from deep holes in the rocks. A length or so of rubber tubing will siphon off water from potholes and tide pools. Where they are available, lengths of kelp, fitted together, substitute for rubber tubing. Collect in small pools while the larger ones are emptying.

48

In Water Too Deep For Wading

Face mask essential. Snorkle, flippers, "float" optional.

The equipment needed for collecting in water too deep for wading depends on your skill, energy, and pocketbook. A face mask is essential. Until you have had much practice in diving, your time below is limited, so make the most of it by investing in a good face mask, one with a glass plate, not plastic. A good snorkle and flippers are a great help in making it possible for you to cruise with greater ease over a larger area, and to reach the bottom quickly with a few powerful scissor-kicks; but these pieces of equipment are expensive, and if you are not going to be able to use them enough to get your money's worth from them, you'd better plan on less expensive gear and a little more physical effort.

On a small Styrofoam "surfing" board, an inflated rubber mattress or life preserver, you may float silently over the bottom to spot your game. A longhandled dip net is useful if the specimens you seek are not too small or the water too deep. If you are a good diver, slide off your float and dive. If you are not so skilled, try expelling air from your lungs. You sink easily to the bottom—or can learn to in time. It takes a bit of practice.

Scuba diving.

Mechanical diving gear is widely available for rent, but attempting to use it without the approval of your physician and a training course by a qualified instructor, is inviting disaster. *Novices are urged to heed this warning.*

Deep water game bag.

In water over-the-head, some experienced collectors use a lightweight cloth bag long enough to loop over a belt. Others use a floating container: a bushel basket from a grocery store set in a circular rubber life preserver with a light cord attached to it and whatever is used for an anchor, a rock or a piece of metal.

Do *not* tie the cord to yourself! There is too much danger of having it become entangled on a submerged object, rock, or coral. Safety is more important than the convenience of trailing your game bag behind you. When you want to move on to another area, it is better to move your anchor.

49

Put several plastic vials in your game bag for small, delicate specimens. In a floating container, there is room for a plastic refrigerator box, or a jar, of sea water for keeping alive specimens you may want to photograph or observe closely later on.

TRAPS

Not wanting to lose an hour of an all-too-short vacation in a good collecting area, some old hands set baited traps. While the shellers collect in other ways, the bait is luring snails whose sense of smell and taste for flesh will be their undoing.

A weighted sack or a fold of wire mesh stuffed with scrap meat or fish heads, is a simple trap for shallow water. They have to be checked frequently because the snails are attracted by the feast but not trapped. They are free to crawl off when they please.

Old tires are also good if drain holes are cut in them to make hauling up easier. A circle of screen wire attached to the underside will prevent the loss of specimens which might be teetering on the rim, headed in or out, just as you happen to haul up. Some collectors who anchored each night in Nassau harbor after dredging by day, let down their baited tires, and took from them in the morning two species of *Cymatium: femorale* (Angular Triton) (see page 86) and *nicobaricum*. The name of this widely dispersed species was derived from the Nicobar Islands.

Another simple trap is a square of ⅛-inch copper screen attached to a rigid frame, two or three feet square, made of pipe or scrap iron. The bait (fish heads, crushed crabs, or mollusks) is put in a ball of wire, to protect it from fish, and fastened to the center of the square. A fisherman's bait-can would do as well. Four cords or wires attached to the corners form a bridle to which a rope is fastened.

These traps, from which snails can easily escape, have to be checked daily. They can be put down in the afternoon and pulled in or up early next morning.

Since carnivorous snails often get into lobster and crayfish traps, local varieties of these traps should be satisfactory for those who can obtain them with ease.

The traps used for *Nautilus pompilius* and fish, called "bo-bos," are made of woven bamboo splints. The entrance is a cone, like that of a rat-trap. There is a door in the bottom for removing the catch.

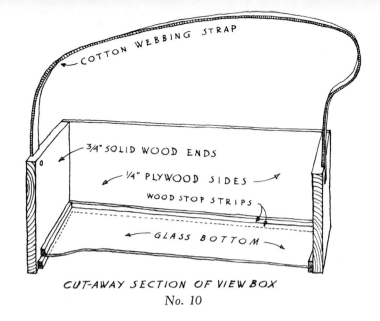

COTTON WEBBING STRAP

¾" SOLID WOOD ENDS

¼" PLYWOOD SIDES

WOOD STOP STRIPS

GLASS BOTTOM

CUT-AWAY SECTION OF VIEW BOX
No. 10

The traps are checked every day, or at intervals of a few days, to renew the bait. One collector reported that he had taken as many as ten specimens at a time from traps baited overnight with the cooked and bruised specimens of crabs.

Two collectors in Cuba have had spectacular success with traps set in deep water. One of them describes his trap as made of strong reed material and ¾₆-inch wire mesh. The reed is ¼-inch wide, and the spaces between the latticework about one inch. There are two ramp-like approaches on the sides, which drop into the trapping area; and in the center is a bait well. The marker is a glass jug. He used fish heads and broken land crabs for bait. The gastropods found in traps of commercial fishermen are carnivorous. Unless the bananas used in Haitian traps have lured them, there is no generally known bait which attracts the herbivorous species.

The Cuban collectors found that rocky or muddy bottoms brought the best results. "The traps can be moved around a bit, but of course luck has much to do with success." A prize specimen turned out to be a beautiful new species, named in honor of one of the trappers, *Murex finlayi.*

"I have taken a great many fine live shells in deep water, but most of the worthwhile things were brought into the traps by hermit crabs," Mr. Finlay wrote me.

Among the crab specimens were some *Charonia variegata* (Atlantic Triton's Trumpet) (see page 137) which were interesting because they were smoother and lighter in structure than the usual specimens from shallower water.

Chapter 11
Helpful Hints

Veteran collectors offer the following suggestions about how and where to collect.

On shallow reefs watch out for octopus holes. They are easily distinguished by the shells littered around the entrance. The octopus slithers over the reef hunting for living mollusks; and, finding what it wants, brings it back home to eat at its leisure. Many of the shells around the holes are very old and covered with marine growths, but collectors frequently report finding fine shells from a recent meal.

In lifting a loose slab of rock, lift the edge *away* from you, just in case a saber-toothed eel may be sheltering under it. If you follow this precaution, the creature will dash away from you rather than into you. It is now thought by qualified observers these animals are not aggressive unless deliberately provoked. An eel's idea of aggression, however, might be putting your hand too close to, or into, the space it calls home.

Examine the underside of a lifted rock for attached bivalves or snails, often in pits. They may be very hard to see because of a coating of marl or because of marine growths covering the shells as well as some of the rock.

Snails may be in plain view on the surface of the sand under the rock. If not, try the veterans' trick of "fanning" the sand to expose buried snails. Or rake through the sand with your crowbar or garden fork, never a bare hand! Some of the choice under-rock species, the beautiful cone shells, Conidae, must not only be handled with care, but approached with care. The dozen or so species known to be poisonous are found in the Indo-Pacific Province. Nevertheless, it is prudent to be cautious in handling all cone shells as you will see in Chapter 17.

In shallow-water collecting, veterans are alert to all the telltale signs that less experienced eyes might ignore: a delicate trail, a tunnel,

52

a depression, a hill of sand. Just at the turn of the tide veterans become particularly watchful.

We have found the shore-side of an exposed west coast Florida sandbar covered with short, grooved trails twisting, looping. In the bump at one end of each, we dug out a tiny *Olivella* (dwarf olive). These tunnel easily through soft wet sand. As the sand dries with the falling tide, however, it becomes more and more difficult for the mollusks to move. Finally they are entombed in igloos of hard sand.

On this same bar we found two-inch *Terebra dislocata* (Common Atlantic Auger), trapped in drying mounds of coarse sand, the foot embedded in the top of the mound, the apex of the shell lying in the trough of the v-shaped trail ending at the mound's base. It was easy to see what had happened. As long as the sand had been moist, the slender little snail could plow under the surface. As the sand became drier, it began to accumulate in front of the foot as snow does in front of a snowplow. Eventually the load became too great. The snail, literally stopped in its track, was trapped until the returning tide released it.

Some shell trackers boast such skill that they can easily distinguish between the trails of closely related species, so that they can pass up those of the common and devote the precious low-tide hours to the less common.

Yet it is frequently rewarding to follow a common trail, if its maker is known to be a voracious predator, because the snail might be dining on a bivalve which might not be found in any other way.

Trails on exposed flats and bars are easily followed; those in water are more of a challenge. In calm weather they may last as long as twenty-four hours. In rough weather they may be covered over in a few hours with sand which the waves have stirred up.

"One type of collecting which we found very fruitful in some of the Pacific Islands," a collector wrote me, "is early morning 'trailing.' Things like *Terebra* (turret shells) and *Oliva* (olive shells) come to the surface of the sand at night. From daybreak to about seven or eight o'clock we found their trails very easy to see in the slanting light of a low sun. We have had particularly good collecting on big sand flats inside the barrier reefs, by swimming along in water from three to ten feet deep, spotting a trail, and digging out the beast at the end. At that time of day they were just under the surface of the sand. By ten o'clock the show was over. They go down deeper, and the sun gets so high there is no shadow in the trough of the trail and it 'disappears.' In other places we could trail all day."

Another trail-tracker wrote that his greatest thrill while hunting mollusks in a South Pacific lagoon was pulling "marlinespike" shells (*Terebra maculata*) out of the sand as one would carrots from a garden. These creamy shells with rust-colored spots, or *maculations* (which inspired the specific name), are much like carrots in size and shape except that the big end is down instead of up.

Although bivalves do not leave long trails like univalves, they nevertheless leave signs for the wise to read. Those not discovered by their extended siphons, may sometimes be traced by depressions or "dimples" in the sand. In the very still, clear water of a tide pool on an exposed bar, we have "fanned" away the sand in a dimple and seen the rims of parted valves, the mantle between them with stubby siphons, or just holes—gaps in the mantle which function like siphons, one for drawing water in, the other for expelling it. Sand particles swirled above the holes for a moment and then the valves closed quietly, and a film of sand settled over them. The uninitiated would not have guessed that a great cockle, Vanhyning's (*Dinocardium robustum vanhyningi*), lay buried there.

Isolated mounds are also worth investigation. Often they are foolers, made by other animals; but often they are not. A collector in St. Croix reports he has found *Conus stearnsi* on top of little sand hills, one specimen to each hill, just under the surface of the sand.

Mollusks react in different ways to the ebb and flow of the tide. In general, a period of quiet sets in with the ebb, a period of withdrawal and waiting. The buried bivalves retract their siphons; the univalves creep into crevices, hide under ledges or in grass beds, burrow into the bottom to wait. Some, sliding along under the surface, follow—or try to follow—the receding water; some about-face at its turn, and race ahead of its inflow.

With the return of the tide bringing a fresh supply of food and oxygen, this period of quiet ceases. Up come the siphons of some bivalves; sometimes, for some strange reasons, up come the bivalves themselves. Some barely break the surface; others give spectacular performances. *Cardium* and *Laevicardium,* cockles, merely peep out from under a "lid" of sand; *Mactra,* surf clams, and others shoot up. One California collector saw *Solen rosaceus* (Rosy Jackknife) erupt with force enough to fall eight inches from their burrows.

Many gastropods also appear suddenly. When I first heard about this phenomenon, I asked an experienced collector if she had ever observed it. "Oh, yes, the beautiful little *Murex recurvirostris rubidus* (Rose Murex) pops right out of the sand just as the tide turns. Once some appeared in pairs, mating."

Another collector had not associated the popping up with the state of the tide, but he did say that he always looked for this species at the very edge of the water. It might be inferred from this that this *Murex* follows the falling tide and emerges at the water's edge just at the turning point.

Following the advice of both collectors, when we next searched a likely sand flat we kept a sharp lookout at the water's edge at the turn of the tide, and were rewarded with a handsome *Conus flori-*

A living Strombus pugilis alatus *(Florida Fighting Conch) showing the long snout (proboscis) flanked by long eyestalks, and the long, narrow foot. The scythe-like operculum is attached to the rear just below the author's little finger. The outer-coat, periostracum, is thin and rather like velvet in texture.*

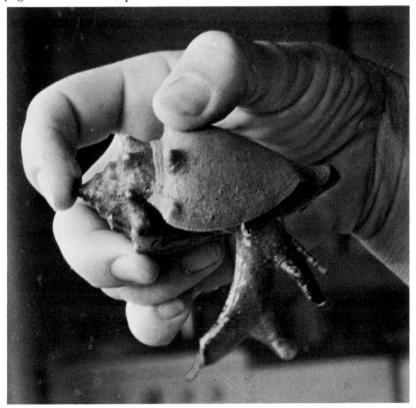

danus burryae (Burry's Florida Cone) which popped into view. The white and orange *Conus floridanus* is a moderately common species; the subspecies *burryae,* a dark color form, is uncommon.

After this experience we remembered two occasions when their emerging with the rising tide may have explained our finding shells on the way back over the flats which had been bare on the way out.

We had gone to great trouble to reach the first bar, and so were particularly disappointed to find it bare except for a few *Melongena* (crown shells) at the edge. It was not large. With two of us to search, we covered it thoroughly. On our way back, we noticed blisters on the smooth surface. Inspecting the nearest one, we found it cracked open, revealing a half-buried *Strombus pugilis alatus* (Florida Fighting Conch). In all of the others we found these same mollusks.

On the second bar we found a number of species as we went out, but not the *Sinum perspectivum* (Lady's Ear) that we hoped for. On our return, with the tide flowing in behind us, we found them lying about in the muddy sand like fat white oysters removed from their shells.

It was with much interest then that I read that a California collector had had the same experience with the *Sinum* of her coast. She has found also that certain *Terebra* and *Drilla* remain hidden as the tide falls, and pop up as it turns.

Whatever the explanation for the sudden appearance of mollusks just at, or after, the turn of the tide, it is a boon to the collector!

Experienced collectors know that scurrying hermit crabs are worth a careful look, especially when the collecting spot is near deep water. These crabs have elongated, soft bodies—and no shell for protection. Dead snail shells, to be had for the taking, make ideal "suits of armor." On finding a snail shell of the right size, the crab winds its long, soft rear end around the inner spiral *(columella)* of the snail shell and is well armed for the battle of life. When it outgrows one shell, a larger one must be found. Thus, hermit crabs change their protective suits a number of times; and any time a change is made by a crab living near deep water, the new shell may be a species rarely found in shallow water.

Collectors working around the west end of New Providence Island, off one of the deepest marine canyons of the Bahamas, told of such luck. They found—above the high tide line—a hermit crab dressed in the delicate, ornate shell of a *Typhis* (tī′ffs) *fordi,* a real treasure.

Some collectors, therefore, take advantage of the gregariousness of hermit crabs. Finding dozens crowded together on or by rocks, or near mangrove roots, the veterans scoop the whole crowd into the collecting bag to be sorted over at leisure after the return of the tide. The specimens not wanted are returned to their rocks by all conscientious collectors.

No. 11

Chapter 12
Dangers and Discomforts

With common sense most dangers and discomforts encountered by shell collectors can be avoided. Take seriously the following *dos* and *don'ts:*

1. Memorize the rules for safe boating. If you rent a boat, insist on a life preserver for everyone, and oars and oarlocks in addition to a motor. All sorts of things can go wrong with a motor—or the person aboard who may be the only one who knows how to run it. In unfamiliar waters where there may be shoals and bad currents, it is best to have a guide who knows about them.
2. Don't get badly sunburned. Use a protective lotion and wear a shirt if you burn easily.
3. Don't put your hands into holes and crevices.
4. Don't pick up, or touch, with bare hands the odd or pretty things you may see. Many are poisonous. Wear gloves.
5. Watch out for stingrays when wading. They lie lightly buried in sand. Usually they are aware of your approach before you are aware of their presence, and dart away. But you can't depend on this. The danger from a stingray is the barb on the tail with which the creature can stab the wader.
6. Watch out for long-spined, black sea-urchins, *Diadema*. Stay well away so that an unexpected surge or loss of balance won't throw you against these brittle, painful spikes. It is said that vinegar will dissolve them, or that hot candle wax will draw them out. Perhaps. Play safe; keep your distance.
7. Beware of Portuguese Men-of-War. They are beautiful—blue bladders with pink, crinkled crests and long, trailing blue tentacles, but very dangerous. Most tentacles are shorter, but some are as long as thirty feet. Tentacles of various jellyfish sting and burn; those of the Man-of-War are so poisonous that even when dead and dried on the beach they can cause a severe pain if

touched. Living ones produce a shock like that of an electric wire which may be followed by cramps, dizziness, nausea, and numbness. The bladders are easily seen; the length of the trailing tentacles must be remembered. In case of an accidental entanglement, call a doctor.

8. Beware of scorpion fishes. The most to be feared in this family of fishes is, happily, not encountered in the waters of the American mainland. If, however, luck should give you a collecting trip in parts of the Indo-Pacific Province, it is to your advantage to be forewarned.

The "stonefish" *Synanceja,* belonging to the family of scorpion fishes, is found in the tropical waters of the Indian and Pacific Oceans. Its hideous warty skin is a perfect camouflage against the rubble of coral and stone above which it lies motionless. Sheathed in the wrinkled skin there is a row of—appropriately—thirteen blue spikes sharp enough to pierce the sole of a tennis shoe. The pressure of the foot forces a virulent poison up through the grooved spines causing instant, agonizing pain; and sometimes death.

For this reason, my Australian friends wear heavy-soled boots when they collect on their great flat reefs. They must also be wary on muddy shores where they have collected the beautiful *Murex monodon* (see page 60). In a letter accompanying a specimen sent to us, one collector wrote: "This species comes into shallow water to breed and is found where there is muddy sand over rock. The snails bury themselves in the mud and may sometimes be detected at low water by the tip of a spine breaking the surface, but you do not put your fingers into the mud. You feel around with a blunt knife because you might find yourself digging up a small stonefish!"

Be warned, but don't be frightened. Thousands of people roam the reefs "fossicking," some of them collecting shells. During Australia's gold rush days, the verb "to fossick" was imported from the mother country, and meant "to prospect," to search for gold. Today, exploring the Great Barrier Reef, marveling at its wonders, is called "fossicking"; and yet there are not many reports of injury from the dreaded "stonefish," perhaps because fossickers are cautious.

Scorpion fishes—beautiful, lacy and marvelously camouflaged—are found in the Florida Keys, Caribbean, and the Gulf of Mexico usually on a hard bottom near reefs. We, however, have never encountered one; nor do we know of any collector who has. Marine scientists who frequent such places constantly urge collectors not to take any chances; to wear shoes and keep their eyes open. Our species are not known to be as fearful as the stonefish, but are poisonous and some may be dangerously so.

Collectors would do well to read, and carry with their field guides, a little booklet published by the Marine Laboratory of the University of Miami called *Sea Pests* (see Bibliography). Its cost is nominal, its value is great. It introduces the novice to harmful sea life, and suggests precautions and remedies. Even though the species it discusses, primarily, are found in the warm water of the western Atlantic coasts, their counterparts are found on other coasts.

A final precaution may save collectors from another kind of unfortunate encounter: the law. Some states require collecting licenses just as they do hunting, fishing and boating licenses; others don't. State laws are far from uniform about what you may and may not collect; and also not easily understood because of the frequent use of popular names like "clams," "winkles," "cockles." All clams or certain clams? Which "winkles"? By "cockles" does the law refer to certain species of the family to which *Cardium* shells belong; or does it mean *any* two-shelled mollusk—a bivalve?

The names of the agencies concerned with state laws vary. They may be: Departments, Commissions, Divisions, of: Conservation, Marine Fisheries, Fish and Game, Shellfisheries.

Check with local collectors, officers of shell clubs, or Chambers of Commerce. A state without a law last year, may have one now. Last year's law may have been amended. Play safe and find out.

No. 12

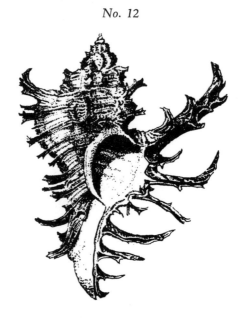

Chapter 13
Beauties of
the Back Bays

You think of looking for seashells on the seashore or in the sea; yet some of the most beautiful and interesting seashells are found in lagoons and back bays. Bay and lagoon species have almost complete protection from violent wave action; but other factors make life difficult.

These shallow water species are subject to greater changes in temperature—water hotter in hot weather and colder in the cold. Its saltiness varies with the amount of rain; with the size of the streams, if any, emptying into the inlet; with the width and depth of the opening to the sea through which salt water pours with the flowing tide. During low or minus tides, flats and bars may be exposed, or nearly so. When seaward winds coincide with a falling tide, the whole area may be drained of water. Shellers call this "coming dry."

The species found in such places are hardy ones which have adapted to a "climate" that may swing quickly from one extreme to another.

Some intertidal animals have a most amazing way of coping with the hazards of their environment. It is a protective device against predators or from falling rocks and tides. Pinned down, a crab or brittle star will deliberately break off a claw or tentacle. Another will grow to replace it. Some ribbon worms simply cannot be picked up. On being touched, they "go all to pieces."

This process is called *au-tot'o-my.* The word comes from two Greek words meaning *self* and *cutting.* Literally it means: self-division.

Some mollusks have developed this remarkable protective device. The Pacific coast *Solen rosaceus,* a jackknife clam, uses this device as a defense from overexposure. It is at home on sand flats and is cursed with such long, annulated or "ringed" siphons that they

A minus tide in a muddy bay. The author searches a bed of 'coon oysters for Melongena corona (Crown Shells). Note specimens by her right foot.

cannot be fully withdrawn into the protecting shells. Exposed by a minus tide to preying shore birds, the clam sloughs off "ring" after "ring" of its siphons until they are safely out of sight. Gulf of California collectors report that a little known species of octopus (*Octopus alecto*) casts off a tentacle when annoyed. Pursued by a predator, or collector, the beautiful *Harpa* (harp shells) shed the rear portion of the foot. One authority says it is apparently cut off by pressure of the shell. Australian collectors add two more species to the roster of gastropod autotomists. One is *Haliotis scalaris* (Staircase or Three-ribbed Abalone) and the snail *Gena auricula*. "One may turn a rock and see dozens of these small snails scuttling off to safety, shedding bits and pieces as they go—to tempt and halt the pursuer, I suppose."

The motto of the animals practicing autotomy is: Divide and live, a reversal of the warning in the famous cartoon of American Revolutionary times which showed a scotched snake, each section named for one of the thirteen states, with the caption: Join or die.

The bottoms of protected inlets vary greatly from mud to sand, or a mixture of the two. Some are grassy; some are strewn with rubble; some have oyster beds, thus they attract a great variety of species which live there throughout the year. Some deep water species come into such shallow, sheltered waters to breed.

The accessibility and relative safety of bay and lagoon collecting makes these areas fine hunting grounds for beginners. Many have not been explored carefully enough, some not at all. There are rarities to be found, and discoveries to be made.

A careful reading of a field guide for the coast you plan to collect on will give you many helpful hints about what you may expect to find where. Again and again you will find descriptions like these: "on eel grass or rocks of bays and coves"; "common in sandy bays"; "found in the low-tide zone of mud flats"; "on mud flats"; and "on rocky shores."

Here are some examples of the possibilities. Some of these species have a limited range along the coast; others may be found all the way from New England to Texas, from Oregon to southern California.

At low tide some grassy mud flats from Cape Cod to the tip of Texas may seem abloom with little lemon-yellow blossoms—Morton's Egg Cockle, *Laevicardium* (laevi-cardium) *mortoni*. The two cupped valves look like petals. Many valves are patterned with brown zigzag lines inside and on the creamy outside. Lazy or hurried collectors content themselves with the prettiest, freshly dead specimens. Other collectors search for living specimens in the mud.

Tellina alternata (Alternate Tellin) is another pretty bivalve with a great range. The valves are delicately ridged and may be white, yellow, or pink. (See Frontispiece, upper right).

Shallow, muddy bays in Florida are often showered with Rose Petals *(Tellina lineata)*. These tiny tellins are white or deep pink. The valves have an opalescent sheen outside; the inside is smooth and the pink of the colored ones is richer. (See Frontispiece, upper left).

Another species in this family, Tellinidae, may be found from North Carolina to Texas but is a rarity in shallow water. *Tellidora crista* (White Crested Tellin) (see page 70) is a delicate, dime-sized bivalve whose concentric ridges end in sharp points along the hinged side, creating a saw-toothed edge. The specimens in our collection were dredged in three feet of water over a bottom of sandy mud and grass.

A beautiful bivalve found in the south half of Florida and the West Indies is the Atlantic Pearl Oyster *(Pinctata radiata)*. Our best specimens came from a grassy mud flat in the Florida Keys. I was about to check off as a failure the afternoon's shelling. Each time at this spot we had found something new to us. This time there was nothing. The tide had turned; the flat was already covered with a

63

few inches of water. As I walked slowly toward the mangrove-bordered shore searching the bottom carefully, I began to see dozens of small circular mounds with sharp points edging the spiral from base to spire. I was walking among the stars! All around me Long-spined Star Shells (*Astraea phoebia*) were scattered over, or half buried in, the sandy mud. That was a surprise. Before, we had always found them spangling the satin-like ribbons of eel grass. I put a few stars in my collecting bag and was about to move on when, a foot away, I noticed a delicate green, fern-like seaweed swaying gently above the jagged rocks or coral on which it grew. As I watched it, some of the upright flanges opened slightly. Suddenly I could "see" what I had been staring at. The jagged patch decked with the seaweed was not coral or rock, but a bed of tightly packed bivalves! They were standing upright, like compacts on their rims. When I tried to pick one up, I had to pull hard, and found it anchored to the bottom by strong, elastic byssus threads.

We collected several dozen specimens ranging in size from an inch in diameter to two inches and a half. When they had been washed, cleaned, and laid out to dry, we saw how different these were from the beach specimens we had found. The latter were smooth on the outside; inside, the pearly lining reached the rim of each valve.

On the outside, the living specimens were covered with delicate spines which overlapped like shingles. As they approached the rim, they grew longer; at the edge they projected as much as a quarter of an inch. On the inside we saw that the lustrous mother-of-pearl lining of the valves was rimmed with a wide, brittle white border striped with black, from which the long spines radiated. Until we saw them with our own eyes, the description of these in our field guide meant nothing.

We preserved the byssus of most of the specimens, but the fragile seaweed with which they had been masked dried and crumbled. These shells are displayed butterfly fashion in Riker Mounts to protect the brittle spines. Some are opened to show the inside of the valves, some are turned to show the interesting outside. Each has its byssus placed by the notch through which it grew.

There are three varieties of Atlantic Bay Scallop, the edible scallop of the East Coast. Each has a limited range, but together they stretch from Nova Scotia to Texas. Displayed together, they show the interesting variations between the northern species and the two southern subspecies. They are:

Aequipecten irradians irradians   Nova Scotia to Long Island, N.Y.
(aequi-pecten ir-ra-di-ans)
Aequipecten irradians concentri-   New Jersey to Georgia, western
cus (con-cen-tri-cus)   Florida to eastern Texas
Aequipecten irradians amplico-   Central Texas to Mexico and
status (am-pli-co-sta-tus)   Colombia

Irradians is the most compressed of the three, and the most colorful. The white, ribbed shell is richly marked with shades of brown and dark gray, sometimes splashed with yellow. Most are like this, but very gay ones occur—yellow, peach, orange.

Both *amplicostatus* and *concentricus* are fatter than *irradians*. With each the lower valve is more cupped than the top and is lighter in color, often snow white. The top valves are mottled with bluish gray and brown. *Concentricus* has more ribs than the northern variety; and the Texas variety has fewer and heavier ribs than either of the others (see page 45).

Among the most attractive back bay univalves are:

Busycon canaliculatus—Channeled Whelk

Turbo castaneus—Chestnut Turban

Conus spurius atlanticus—Alphabet Cone

Conus floridanus—Florida Cone

Conus stearnsi—Stearns' Cone

Murex florifer—Lace Murex

Murex florifer arenarius—White Lace Murex

Look these up in your field guide and see which are near you, and note the preferred habitat: mud, sand, grass, rocks or mangrove.

Some species, like *Murex florifer,* can be found in all these habitats. On mud flats or around mangrove roots this beautiful shell is some shade of brown; on protected rocks it may be quite light. Those from sandy areas are the white variety: *arenarius.* The name comes from the Latin word *arena:* a sandy place. The white specimens are usually not as frilly as the dark ones; but, when young, have peach-pink spires. One more habitat should be added to those listed: oyster beds. We have found this *Murex* species swarming over beds of 'coon oysters around little mangrove cays.

We have found the Alphabet and Florida Cones on mud banks between mangrove-bordered islands; and tiny, lovely Stearns' Cones came up in the dredge with the White Crested Tellins.

In brackish water 'coon oysters (*Ostrea frons*) dangle in bunches from the splayed red roots of mangrove trees; in saltier water you

65

The author's collecting partner hauling in the dredge.*

find Flat Tree Oysters (*Isognomon alatus*) hanging in tightly packed clusters from the roots. Each bivalve is attached to the root, if there is space, by its byssus; if not, it anchors itself to the shell neighbor above or beside.

Outside, this bivalve is very ugly, dull brown or purple, and flaky. Inside, the brown and purple have a pearly sheen. This species is closely related to the Atlantic Wing Oyster and Pearl Oyster (*Pteria colymbus* and *Pinctada radiata*). The straight hinge has eight to twelve oblong, straight-sided grooves, each of which is set with a small brown resilium to push the valves apart.

Don't stop your collecting at the roots of mangroves. Look up in the branches. A *seashell* up a tree? Yes, and one of the prettiest species: *Littorina angulifera* (Angulate Periwinkle), sturdy but thin, gracefully spiraled snails. Most are honey-brown marked with darker, wavy lines; some are pale gold or cream; some apricot, some dark red. This species spends most of its life high above high-tide zone on wharf pilings as well as mangrove roots but must return to the sea to spawn.

Beside many interesting species to be found in the protected bays

*,For excellent information on dredging in shallow and deep water see *How To Collect Shells*, a publication of the American Malacological Union.

"A seashell up a tree?" The author collecting Angulate Periwinkles (Littorina angulifera) *from the branches of a mangrove tree in a back bay of southern Florida. These beautiful snails are found throughout the Caribbean Province.*

of the Pacific coast, five or six beauties may be found in the low-tide zone of mud flats and sandbars. Four of them belong to families which are favorites with collectors: Cypraeidae (sī-prē′ĭ-dē), cowries and related species; Muricidae (mū-rǐs′ĭ-dē), murexes and related species; and Conidae (cŏn′ĭ-dē), the cones.

The cowry of Southern California, *Cypraea spadicea* (Chestnut Cowry) (see page 134) is the most colorful one of the mainland. The base is white, the hump is amber with a dark, irregular border separating this color from the bluish-lavender sides. This snail is moderately common at certain seasons. Search for it at low tide among sea weeds.

Conus californicus (California Cone) is small and yellow-brown with a band of bluish-white; the periostracum is velvety and reddish-brown.

The two murexes are: *Murex trialatus* (Western Three-Wing Murex) and Nuttall's Thorn Purpura or "purple" snail, whose Latin first name came from a word meaning "wing" or "having wings": *Pterorytis* (the *p* is silent) *nuttalli*. Some field guides list this species under a name meaning horn- (*Cerata*) mouth (*stoma*).

67

Tunneling under mud in search of bivalves to devour is round, yellowish-brown *Polinices lewisi* (Lewis' Moon Snail); and tunneling in soft sand is beautiful *Olivella biplicata* (Dwarf Purple Olive). The shell is lavender, the indented spiral line amber. The name *bī-pli-cá'tá* was inspired by the two folds, *plica* (plī'kà) [meaning *a fold*], on the inner lip.

For the scallop lovers, the Pacific coast is a happy hunting ground. There are exquisitely colored ones—pink, pink and white, dark red, peach and bright yellow—with and without fine spines—to be had in shallow water or by dredging (see color plate). In bays and rocky inlets collectors may find:

Chlamys hindsi (Hind's Scallop), rose, mauve, lemon, orange, extends from Alaska to San Diego.

Aequipecten circularis (Round Scallop) is a plump bivalve with a wide variety of colors from white to orange, brown and purple. It is found in eel grass lightly buried in sand. This is the Pacific coast analogue—parallel, equivalent or "twin"—of the fat, brightly colored Calico Scallop *(Aequipecten gibbus)* found in abundance on the Atlantic coast from North Carolina south to the West Indies.

The Giant Rock Scallop, *Hinnites multirugosus* (mul-ti-ru-go'sus), is naturally found where there are rocks to which to attach itself. The young, sometimes brightly colored, are delicate and hard to distinguish from some species of *Chlamys*, on the outside. Inside, some have a purplish spot on each side of the resilium pit at the hinge line. Mature specimens are massive and often distorted in shape because of being crowded.

A note accompanying three specimens sent us by a collector in Seattle is of interest and gives helpful hints to novice collectors.

"These bivalves are usually found in small holes or caves under overhanging rocks; and are so covered with marine growths that they are next to impossible to spot unless they are at least partly open so that you can see the bright orange mantle. Collecting them is hard work. They have to be chipped out with a screwdriver and hammer.

"The largest specimen (six inches from hinge to rim) was completely trapped in a hole which it must have entered when it was young and small. This explains its odd, bulging shape. It took a lot of chipping to get it out.

"My collecting partner called out that he had found another, the medium-sized specimen; but when I joined him he had 'lost' it. We

Foreground: *Chlamys hastatus* (Pacific Coast Spear Scallop); background: *Chlamys hericius* (Pacific Coast Pink and Yellow Scallops).
John Lewis Stage

could see nothing. We waited patiently by the hole until the valves parted again and we saw the bright mantle. We had to knock off a square foot of rock to get this one out."

Keep in mind that from early spring and often throughout the summer, deep-water species may be in the bays for breeding. This opportunity to collect for yourself something you might never be able to get otherwise places an obligation on the collector to limit his "take." You may see egg cases about and if you can identify them positively as those of the deep-water species, you can collect more shells with an easy conscience. If you do not see egg cases, or can't tell one kind from another, then master that impulse to take "just one more," and another and another. The mature shells may just have arrived, and not had the opportunity to breed.

As interesting as it is to get what you know is there, or may be there, coming on something completely unexpected makes the day a red-letter one.

On a mud bar in an inlet on the east coast of Florida we came on dozens of that state's Fighting Conch (*Strombus pugilis alatus*) popping out of the mud at the turn of the tide. We examined every specimen, found them all alive, and took two specimens for the

A cluster of egg capsules made by Murex pomum *(Apple Murex) a colorful, common species found in shallow water in the southeastern United States, the Bahamas, and the West Indies.*

record, since we had many others in our collection from other places. Walking back to our skiff, I spotted a new pop-up which seemed to have better color than those in our bag and leaned over for a closer look. It was not the rust-brown Florida subspecies at all, but the apricot-colored species, *Strombus pugilis*, common in the West Indies but rare in Florida, and getting more so. Increasing water pollution and perhaps over-collecting in an inlet where it was once abundant, and channel-dredging in another good collecting spot, are making this species more of a rarity on the mainland. We went over the bar again but found no other. Our single specimen was a very lucky find.

No. 13

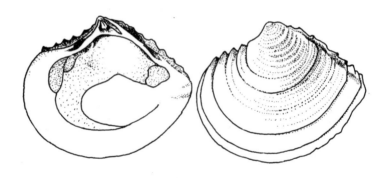

Chapter 14
Beauties of
the High Seas

Some of the most beautiful seashells are creatures of the open sea, so made that they can live their entire lives floating on the surface of oceans—and do, unless blown ashore by high winds and hurricanes.

They were well known to sailors of old whose ships were often motionless like the Ancient Mariner's "painted ship upon a painted ocean." What luck for the idle seamen if a great colony of beautiful and strange creatures drifted by slowly enough for the men to see them well.

There might be hundreds of blue bladders with ruffled pink crests and trailing tentacles of blue; and stiff little rafts of shiny blue, each set with a triangular, silvery "sail." The men made up names for them. The great crested bladders reminded them, naturally enough, of full-rigged sailing ships. They became known as "Portuguese Men-of-War." The little rafts with a fixed fin for a sail were called Jack-Sail-by-the-Winds. Unable to set their "sails" to take advantage of the winds, the Jacks went where the winds blew them or the currents carried them.

Often among the Jacks and Men-of-War there were countless clusters of transparent, glistening bubbles, silvery-blue, with something hanging from each of them. Perhaps one sailor more curious than the rest scooped up some of the bubble-clusters and found that a violet-colored shell swung from each. Some bubble-clusters were flat, like rafts; some were shaped like a curved horn, tapering from the large end to the tip. The shells were slightly different in shape, too, but they were all spiraled like the snails in gardens at home, so they became "Purple-Sea-Snails."

Some of the drifters in the ocean were little "boats" of crinkled, nearly transparent white shell in each of which a big-eyed creature crouched. This curious "boatman" looked like an octopus—exactly like the octopuses slithering around the rocks of the home ports, constantly caught, dried in the sun, and served on many a table.

"Well, not exactly," a more observant sailor may have said, pointing to one of the creatures he had scooped up. "An octopus has eight 'arms,' or tentacles, with sucker-disks. This fellow has six octopus-like arms, but look at the other two!" These were broad and flat at the ends.

"Like hands," said someone.

"Or wings."

"No, like oars; and no doubt used for rowing. How else would this 'boatman' row his little boat?"

"Those are *sails*; not oars, or wings, or hands."

"Have you ever seen one hoisted to catch the breeze?"

"Well, no. But when we can see them it is because we are becalmed, and they, too. No use to hold up the sail-arms when there's no wind. Our sails hang from the mast and yardarms."

That explanation may have settled many an argument for the time being. Ashore the argument went on. Paddles or sails?

"What is the name of this shell?" The question could have been asked by a delighted wife whose husband had brought her one for a souvenir.

It may have been that the village teacher said that a scholar had said it was a *Nautilus* of some kind. It had to be, because of the shape.

"But paper-thin. You can almost see through it! And crinkled."

The other kind of *Nautilus* was thicker, creamy white with wavy brown lines. Some of those had been brought back by sailors, too.

So this thin crinkled seashell became known as the "Paper Nautilus."

Poets saw both kinds of shells, also, and heard the yarns of the seamen. Oliver Wendell Holmes' fancy was taken by the idea that the arms with broad membranes were "sails" which, in his mind's eye, were the "purpled wings" of "the venturous bark," flung "on the sweet summer wind" in "gulfs enchanted."

He did not know that "the venturous bark," his "ship of pearl," did not have broad-tipped tentacles which might be thought of as "sails" or "wings."

Alexander Pope thought of "the little nautilus" spreading a "thin oar," in a "driving gale."

Poetic imagination added to the confusion of sailors' yarns.

Today seamen of a different kind know these beauties of the high seas better than any mariner of old. Oceanographers catch them in surface tow nets; observe and photograph them in aquariums. These students of the sea are disentangling fact and fancy, and proving that fact is often more fascinating than fiction.

These beautiful mollusks, the Men-of-War, the Jacks, and others are called *pelagic* (pė-lăj'ĭk) species or organisms. The word comes from Greek and Latin words meaning *sea*. Pelagic animals are ones which live, and usually die, at sea.

THE PURPLE SEA SNAILS—*Janthina*

The Purple Sea Snails swinging from the bubble-clusters were formally named by the great eighteenth century Swedish scientist Carl Linnaeus, who perfected the system of classification for plants and animals which is in use today. In naming these shells *Janthina janthina* (jăn'thĭ-nà jăn'thĭ-nà) Linnaeus may have been inspired by the description of a shore where thousands of them had been cast by a high wind and tide. Perhaps one of his many students, roving the world for specimens to take home to the master teacher, told him that after a storm a coast might look as if it were abloom with violet flowers. This idea would have appealed to Linnaeus, who knew and loved flowers, and published books on them. So the name he gave the floating sea snails was made from Greek words meaning *violet* and *flower*.

There are two other species of *Janthina*: a tiny one called *exigua*, meaning dwarf; and a plump one, *globosa*. *Janthina janthina* is the largest and most common of the three. All are found in most warm seas the world over, floating in great colonies, often mingled with Portuguese-Men-of-War (*Physalia*, fĭ-sā'lĭ-à), and the little Jack-Sail-by-the-Winds (*Velella*, vė-lĕl'à). They are thrown on our southern coasts: Atlantic, Gulf, and Pacific. Sometimes they appear in New England and occasionally all the way across to the British Islands.

Once cast ashore they are doomed. These snails have a foot, but it is not one which can be used for creeping back to the sea. Lucky is the collector who comes on a beach strewn with living *Janthina*. Put some of them in a jar of water and study them. You will see that the shell hangs top-side down from the bubble raft; and that the foot is a cupped appendage to which the bubble-cluster is at-

73

tached (see page 80). The snail's foot makes the float by secreting a clear mucous which entraps bubbles of air and congeals on touching the sea and air. The eggs of the female snail are attached to the underside of the float of bubbles. The young emerge as little snails with shells.

The shell of the dwarf species is lavender; that of *globosa* is a rich, shining purple; and that of *Janthina janthina* is half and half. The top side, where you see the spiral begin, is a pale, milky lavender; the underside is dark purple. Perhaps this is protective coloration. The pale side blends with a hungry fish's view of the surface; and the dark side blends with the blue-purple of the sea to protect the defenseless snails from birds of prey.

Although the Purple Sea Snails are drifters at the mercy of currents and winds, because they have no power of movement and are blind; they are able to find food in addition to *plankton*, which may be part of their menu. *Plankton* is the name given to the billions of tiny plants, animals, and eggs or feebly swimming young of larger animals, which live in the surface waters of the sea. Purple Sea Snails have been observed eating some of their pelagic neighbors, the little Jacks *(Velella)*.

Hanging from the underside of the raft-like *Velella* is a central mouth, the main feeding organ, which is surrounded by many bud-like polyps (some of which have mouths, too, as well as stinging cells) and a fringe of tentacles. The stinging cells and tentacles are for capturing and fanning to the many mouths the tiny planktonic organisms on which the Jack lives.

An English oceanographer caught in a plankton tow net a number of *Velella* and *Janthina janthina* and put them in an aquarium aboard the research vessel, R. R. S. *Discovery II*. He found some purple snails attached to the underside of many of the little glistening blue *Velella*. A closer look showed that—like cows in a pasture—the snails were "browsing" on the polyps and tentacles. Off and on, the snails doused the uneaten appendages with a purple fluid which may have anaesthetized the *Velella*. They seemed lifeless, yet they did not shed their tentacles as they usually do when they die.

As an experiment, the observer dropped into a jar of preservative several lively *Velella* and some of those seemingly lifeless ones which had been flooded with the purple secretion. The lively ones reacted as he expected, by violently contracting their tentacles. Those which had been attacked by the snails reacted very weakly.

74

Eventually the *Janthina* in the aquarium ate the little *Velella* rafts clean and they dropped to the bottom of the tank, dead.

Sometimes high winds blow ashore one of these great pelagic colonies—Men-of-War, little Jacks, and all three kinds of *Janthina*. Twice we have had the good luck to see this occurrence.

THE PAPER ARGONAUTS—*Argonauta*

Sitting beside an aquarium in Italy more than a hundred years ago, Madame Jeanette Power solved a mystery about which scientists as well as seamen had argued and speculated for centuries: What kind of creature produces the fragile shell called the "Paper Nautilus" (*Argonauta*) which men saw "sailing" in fleets on the blue Mediterranean, and often found abandoned on the shore? Was it made by a snail and taken over by the octopus-like creature often found with it, as some empty snail shells are taken over by the hermit crabs?

The silent aquarium watcher gave them the answer. She saw a cluster of eggs taken from an *Argonauta* shell hatch as mere specks. As they grew, it was obvious that the young were not snails but tiny, shell-less creatures with eight tentacles: octopods. Later some of the young began to hold together two of the tentacles which were different from the others. Each of these specialized tentacles ended in a broad, oval flange, not unlike a hand.

Between these "hands," held "palm to palm," a gelatinous material appeared. In time the soft substance hardened into thin shelly plates which were joined together along the spiraled margin with a flat keel studded regularly with brown knobs. The spacing of the knobs corresponded with the suckers by which it seemed the knobs had been formed. The newly made shell was a tiny replica of the crinkled, paper-thin *Argonauta*. These specimens continued to grow, and eventually produced egg clusters. The others never produced a shell and were soon outstripped in size.

An octopod, then, not a snail, produced the delicate shell and was the female of the species. Observation, not speculation, solved the mystery.

Some years later a second mystery in the life history of the *Argonauta* was solved. A whip-like object, about four or five inches long, often found in the mantle cavity of the female, had puzzled naturalists for years. Sometimes they saw it wiggling. One of the most eminent French scientists decided it was a new kind of parasitic worm; and as scientists do when they think they have found a new species, he published a paper on the "worm" and named it *Hectocotylus* (hĕc-tō-kŏt'ĭ-lŭs), meaning: hollow vessel.

A Swiss scientist, however, discovered that some of the "worms" were far from empty; they were filled with sperm cells. He jumped to the conclusion that he had discovered the male *Argonauta* and rushed his paper to the printer. Somehow he failed to notice that his "male" had no organs for breathing, digestion, locomotion or direction.

In 1853, a German biologist, Heinrich Mueller, was examining several of the little tentacled creatures which hatched from *Argonauta* eggs, but never produced a shell and remained midgets, one-tenth the size of the shell-producing octopods. On one of the tentacles of one specimen he noticed a swollen sac. When he opened it, out popped the five-inch, whip-like object which had been called a parasitic worm and the male of the species.

Observation of other specimens showed that at certain times of the year the "whip" became violently agitated and burst open its sac. The "whip" looked like the tentacle of octopuses which was known to be the male reproductive organ; but since this *Argonauta* arm was so often found filled with sperm cells in the female, it must be *detachable;* and the little midget octopod must be the male of the species. Heinrich Mueller solved the second half of the *Argonauta* mystery.

It seems strange that it took so long for this discovery to be made. Scientists were familiar with the works of Aristotle, and he noted as long ago as the fourth century B.C. that in the breeding season one tentacle of all the Mediterranean *"polypi"* (octopuses) swells greatly. The fishermen who caught the *polypi* knew of this swollen arm and its function. Seamen and scientists knew that argonauts and octopuses were very much alike—and yet no one put two and two together until 1853.

The specialized, detachable male tentacle remains in the body of the female until it is emptied of sperm cells and then it is discarded. Once fertilized, each of the eggs is protected by a coating of a viscid substance which hardens, making a mass like a bunch of grapes. The cluster is laid deep in the coil of the shelly "nest" in which the female "sits" protecting the eggs.

In contrast to the rest of the Octopoda, almost invariable described as "ugly" and "repulsive," the *Argonauta* is described as "fairy-like," as delicate as her shell, and constantly suffused with waves of changing color. One aquariumist who had a flock of *Argonauta* floating about, describes them as "trembling" with ever-changing colors: yellow, green, violet, "a most delicate shade of blue," "all tints of brown," subtly shading "to rose, vivid scarlet, or molten silver."

The female's body is covered with tiny pigment areas which expand and contract as water is drawn into the body and expelled through the siphon. As the water is drawn in, the color cells contract and the color fades; as the water is forced out, the cells relax and a wave of color sweeps over the animal. The pulsing colors come and go so quickly, that the effect is one of "continuous heat-lightning."

Recent observations and photographs of two species of argonauts have added fascinating details to the slowly accumulating store of scientific information about these beauties of the open sea. Both were caught, unharmed, in a plankton tow net of a research vessel belonging to the Institute of Marine Science, University of Miami. They were netted off Bermuda in night tows.

The common *Argonauta argo* came in first and was put immediately into an aquarium aboard the ship. The observers saw that it did not "sail" or "row" as the poets imagined; nor did it "swim" with six of the tentacles trailing behind, and the other two holding the shell, as two hands hold a bowl. Artists have shown it so in the past, perhaps basing their drawings on speculations of some naturalists or on inaccurate, or ambiguous, reports of those who watched by aquariums.

The photographic record shows *Argonauta argo* crouched deep in the shell, staring out with huge eyes and all eight tentacles *tucked back into the shell* (see page 78). Presumably the suction cups on the tentacles make it possible to grip the shell firmly from the inside.

Not once in the hour of observation did the argonaut use any of its tentacles for movement. It *bobbed* about just under the surface of the water with the keel of the shell *up*. What little movement it could manage was accomplished by jet propulsion. It changed direction and position by changing the direction of the siphon or funnel through which it forced water. Several times it tilted forward, the siphon turned back, and jetted down several inches for several seconds; and then it bobbed back to the surface. It seems that air trapped in the apex of the shell gives enough buoyancy for the argonaut to float without effort just below the surface of the sea.

Twice during the observation and photography, the argonaut

Argonauta argo (*Common Paper Argonaut*), *with "web" spread over shell.* (See also color plate facing page 1).

covered its shell with the wide membranes (the "sails") of the two uppermost tentacles. These tentacles came out of the shell and slid back over the outside of the shell; and then the attached membrane, or "web," of each expanded until the spreading webs looked "like iridescent silver fluid" flowing over the shell. The arms at the top of the shell turned brilliant blue, faded to lavender, and lit up again as blue. Dark spots appeared on the silvery web (see above).

After forming the shell originally, the webs seem to play some part in detecting the presence of food. An observer at an aquarium in Naples dropped a bit of sardine in the tank and, when it touched the expanded web, one of the tentacles on that side shot out and back over the shell and carried the food to the argonaut's mouth. Having no way to go after the food, argonauts simply drift with it— the millions of planktonic organisms. Anything brushing the silver web may be swept into the mouth.

Perhaps it was seeing argonauts with the webs expanded that gave rise to the belief that they "held" the shell with the webbed tentacles outside, the suckers serving as "fingers" for gripping more firmly.

The rare *Argonauta hians* (Brown Paper Argonaut) (see page 79) treated the observers to a rare sight. When put into the aquarium it sank to the bottom, breathing hard, forcing a cloud of sand-like particles through the siphon. But, unlike grains of sand, they did not settle to the bottom, but began to move erratically about all over the aquarium. The grains of "sand" were infant argonauts! They were almost transparent except for big dark eyes and tiny color spots. The scientists siphoned out some of the babies and studied them under a microscope. They displayed rainbow colors and, when disturbed, erupted with a rash of red spots.

In the meanwhile the mother was becoming exhausted after giving birth to three hundred babies. She flashed rainbow colors and fell on her side. When she did, a bubble of air escaped from her shell. Fearing this disaster would make it impossible for her to rise again, the observers scooped her out of the tank quickly with a net. Evidently alarmed, the animal ejected a cloud of "ink" in the water; and, when out of the water, climbed out of the shell. The would-be rescuers put her back into the shell and into the aquarium but she left the shell again, and soon died.

And so did all three hundred babies. They may have been born prematurely, or have been poisoned by the "ink" in a confined area; or the water in the aquarium may have lacked something they

Argonauta hians (*Brown Paper Argonaut*), *showing shell filled with eggs.* (See also color plate facing page 160).

needed. In the abandoned shell there were many other newly hatched argonauts and eggs in various stages of development.

Argonauts add to their shells as they increase in size and can patch broken places. They are able to leave their shells, but probably do not except in emergencies. It used to be said that the growing eggs "pushed the *Argonauta* right out of her 'nest'"; and that she then "swam" about holding the shell until the eggs hatched—and then, "abandoned the shell," and built another later.

But does she? Perhaps this "fact" is another fancy which further observation will put on the shelf with the others of the past.

No. 14

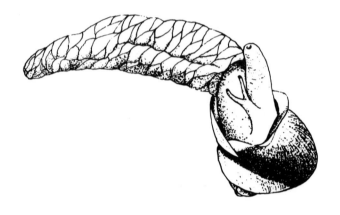

Chapter 15
Collecting on
Atlantic Reefs

Excerpts from a collector's diary
New Providence Island, Bahamas, 1957
August 15:
   One of the roads brought us to a bluff overlooking a picture-book bay with a crescent beach of snowy sand, ending in two rocky promontories.
   A glance at our watches showed that, for better or worse, this was to be today's hunting ground. It was one hour before low tide. The promontories looked encouraging. We started in the direction of the nearest one.
   The approach over eroded coral rock was hazardous (see page 82). The pits which peppered it were rimmed with jagged edges and sharp points, which felt as if they would cut through the rubber soles of our tennis shoes unless we stepped lightly. Falls would have made bloody wrecks of us. Where the rock sloped to the water, there were tide pools filled with several kinds of *Nerita* and young black-and-white *Cittarium pica* (West Indian Top Shell) (see page 158).
   As we waded out, we found to our delight that the rocky point and a bar that extended from it were brilliant with sea fans and whips. When the water was deep enough, we snapped on face masks and for a while literally walked on our hands, our bodies afloat, through the marine garden, close enough to see every colorful detail. It was inexpressibly beautiful.
   The rocky bottom was carpeted with small, burrowing urchins— bright, Chinese-red ones. Some were red with black spines, a few blue-black. There were golden lumps (sponge? coral?), tangled clumps of reddish "finger coral," and patches of vivid green, creeping "seaweeds." There were lime and lavender sea fans, pink and purple whips—all in miniature, dwarfed by the shallow water. The tops of

Author on New Providence Island, Bahamas. Note the jagged coral rock, tide-pool pockets, the essential tennis shoes, the water-glass, gloves, crowbar and face mask.

some of the stiff, lacy fans were seared and brown, sunburned where they had been exposed by extreme low tides. Through the colorful garden and the pale blue-green water, dozens of little fishes darted about in brilliant Mardi Gras costumes—black and white stripes, neon-light blue and red, gold and black, turquoise blue. When we were motionless, they swam all around us. Two kinds were especially pretty. One, no larger than a baby's hand, as broad as it was long, was butter-yellow. The other, long and streamlined, had a turquoise head and gills, an apple-green tail, and a cummerbund about its middle of the palest blue bordered with black.

We swam out to deeper water. I exhaled and sank to the bottom. Glancing up, I seemed to be looking at the underside of a billowing, silvery-blue sheet which shimmered as it lifted and fell. When a wave broke, a shower of silver bubbles shot downward in a curve.

Precious minutes were ticking away. It was time to end the sightseeing and begin the search.

Almost immediately we discovered a pair of *Cyphoma gibbosum* (Flamingo Tongue Cyphoma) at the base of a pale green fan. This was our first sight of the living animals. The shell has a slot on the underside, like a *Cypraea* (cowry) from which the fleshy mantle lobes creep up over the shell until they meet, or almost meet, on the "top" side. The translucent, flesh-colored lobes are closely set with squarish spots of tawny yellow, distinctly defined with a narrow black border. The foot is yellowish, marked with radial lines of black. The siphon, of the same color, flares at the tip like a trumpet.

Delighted with our find, we swam about looking for, finding and collecting others. In nearly every case we found them two to a fan. Later we heard that August is the mating season for this species.

The reef-bar fell away to clean white sand. We swam off in opposite directions. I came on a jumble of rocks like an island in the sand; and went to work, turning—and re-turning each to its former position—but found nothing. They were easily turned, and in loose sand, but there was no sign of life of any kind around or under them—no plants, no animals.

On the other side of the bar my husband's sunburned arm beckoned me. I found him standing waist deep on top of rocks which formed a roughly circular well fifteen feet in diameter in about ten feet of water. Stepping, or leaping from rock to rock, like giants on mountaintops, we went around the rim and peered into the well from every angle. Within the protection of the rocks, the tallest pink and purple sea plumes we had ever seen swayed gently; but the largest black urchins, lodged among the rocks and nestling at the bottom, discouraged any idea of diving to see what mollusks might be on the plumes. There was another deterrent also. Besides the large fish lazily swimming through the rocky grottoes, there well may have been a moray eel or two watching from a hidden recess. It was too small a place to explore with such big urchins and the possibility of big eels.

On our way back to the point, in about five feet of water we found a solitary brown plume growing. My husband dived to examine its base and bobbed up to report the presence of a pair of large *Cyphoma*, "unlike the others."

"Perhaps the *mcgintyi!*"

We had hoped to find a few *Cyphoma mcgintyi* (McGinty's Cyphoma). To untrained eyes, the shell of this species is almost undistinguishable from those found at first, but the mantle and foot are very different. The mantle is pink and bordered, not covered, with irregularly round maroon spots.

To get a good look at my partner's find, I submerged and hung on to his leg. When I was level with the shells I almost drowned

83

gasping with excitement. Their mantles were not marked with yellow squares nor maroon spots, but with fine black lines patterned exactly like an inked fingerprint. These were *Cyphoma signatum* (Finger-print Cyphoma) (see page 87), the rarest of the three species!

While I collected in tide pools my partner swam out again over the sea garden for a second search. When he returned he added a *Charonia variegata* (Atlantic Triton's Trumpet) to our bag. He had found it just under the edge of an uptilted rock so heavily camou-flaged, like the rocks, with marine growths and marl that we had overlooked it the first time.

Our expedition has gotten off to an auspicious start.

August 16:

We explored stations within walking distance of our hotel. The floor of the sea in front of the hotel had been raked clean of all underwater objects which might annoy bathers; but just around the point we found a fine spot, from the sheller's point of view; a place with great meadows of grass joining a rubble area filled with large, loose rocks—and the inevitable long-spined black urchins.

We started in the rocky area first, swimming with face masks, turning the rocks. Best finds, several *Chlamys ornata* (Ornate Scallop) and two small *Murex* shells not then identified. They were in pits in the rocks. The scallops—white dappled with purple—were flat against the undersides, each held fast by the byssus.

For the rest of the time we searched the grass beds in water not quite neck deep so I could walk around peering through the water-glass without breaking my back; and giving my sunburned face relief from the pressure of the face mask, until I saw something to inspect or collect.

At one place where I walked from thick grass into an area of sand with thin patches of grass, I saw just a few feet away a four-foot, mottled-green "snake" slithering toward me. A moray eel, no doubt.

I controlled my first frightened impulse to flee as quickly and quietly as possible from this creature which could *swim* as well as crawl, and remained to watch—fascinated—with only a prudent backing to one side as the creature approached. It was in no hurry; it seemed to be lazily looking around for a mid-morning snack, paus-ing to peer into a clump of grass before sliding around it. There were

84

many holes, and the eel peeped into each one looking for fishes, crabs and mollusks. Usually the foraging is done at night. Perhaps hunting the night before had not been successful.

As soon as its investigations took it far enough beyond me, I followed quietly and watched until it wriggled out of sight, temporarily, because our paths came near crossing again that day. I am indebted to that thorough hunter for one of the best finds of the day. When I next spotted him, still searching lazily, I about-faced, continuing my search in the opposite direction; and within a few minutes saw a beautiful four-inch *Murex florifer* (Burnt Rock Shell). Because of the marl coating it was the color of the sand and rubble, but it was on the surface and the triangular shape and decorative varices were easy to see.

Harry matched my *Murex* with an enormous, beautifully colored *Cassis tuberosa* (King Helmet Shell) (see page 153), the first we had ever found. It was so heavy and big that it presented many problems for island-hopping collectors—cleaning and carrying. He wanted to put it back in the water; I wanted to keep it. He gave in with the understanding that I would clean and carry it, a fair compromise.

The author washing marl and mud off the day's bag.

Left: Cymatium femorale (*Angular Triton*). *This handsome species is widely distributed in the West Indian region. It is not rare, yet specimens do not appear to be common at any one locality. They are usually found a little beyond low water on sandy bottoms where sea grass is abundant. The color varies from golden-brown to reddish-orange.*

Right: This view of Cymatium femorale (*Angular Triton*) *shows the interesting shaggy outer coat, periostracum. Specimens range in size from three to eight and a half inches.*

August 17:

On the first point in the other direction from the hotel, we found a bar of grass and rubble running out toward the ocean. There were many red starfish and patches of feathery "flowers" blooming on slender stems into which the flower heads disappeared at the slightest splash or if our shadows fell across them—tubeworms.

Here in water that ranged from ankle to eye-deep we had a fine day. I was especially pleased with collecting three *Cymatium femorale* (Angular Triton) (see above). All were partly buried in sand patches near pockets of grass. They were covered with a furry greenish periostracum. The mantle lining the lavender aperture was reddish-purple and finely speckled with dots that looked like silver bubbles.

86

Under a rock Harry discovered a *Lima scabra* (Rough File Shell). It was agape with its fringe of red tentacles waving. I hastened over to see it, but before I got there Harry dropped the rock and went plunging through the water away from me. The *Lima* had escaped. It darted off in its zigzag way, Harry in hot pursuit; but, in waist-deep water, he floundered and lost it.

We have ten more days!

No. 15

Chapter 16
Collecting on
a Classic Reef

With jet liners now streaking through the skies, it is possible for an increasing number of people to have the thrilling experience of collecting on a classic reef, a shelf of living, stony coral. The people who have collected on such reefs are spoiled because, at low tide, there are such enormous stretches of wading-depth water teeming with colorful marine animals—among which are hundreds of beautiful shells.

Since the opportunity may come to any reader, it will be interesting to know in advance what reef collecting is like on the greatest reef of all.

Over a hundred years ago Charles Darwin said there appeared to be three kinds of coral reefs: fringing reefs, barrier reefs, and encircling reefs—coral atolls.

The fringing reefs were easily understood. Corals flourish in warm, clear, sunlit—and therefore relatively shallow—water. Fringing reefs fan out from the land in an almost solid shelf. Barrier reefs and atolls rising from great depths, and far from the mainland, were a puzzle. Darwin's solution was brilliant and, with some modifications, is still accepted today.

He reasoned that barrier reefs and atolls had once been fringing reefs; and that, as the land they fringed *sank*, the stony, reef-building corals grew up, up, up, and out—wider and wider, seeking the sunlit part of the sea necessary for their life. Eventually the barrier reef was far at sea, separated from the mainland by a channel or lagoon. And a reef which had fringed a tiny island, often the top of a submerged volcano, eventually enclosed a lagoon, because the volcano-top had disappeared into the sea.

However different their origins, the surfaces of reefs are much the same.

On a map showing distribution of today's coral reefs in the Pacific

88

and Indian Oceans, the black dots by which they are indicated are sprinkled from the Red Sea to Madagascar; they pepper the East Indies; splash north around and beyond the Philippines; and trail southeast over the part of the world we call the "South Seas." In all this area, the greatest concentration of dots forms a dark black line off the northeast coast of Australia. Just off southern Queensland, and stretching north toward New Guinea for well over a thousand miles, is the greatest coral reef in the world, one of its most beautiful natural wonders: the Great Barrier Reef.

The Great Barrier Reef is often spoken of as a coral rampart; but, except for one portion, it is not an unbroken wall. It is made up of a chain of reefs extending from off Cape York in the north to the Swain Reefs in the south. North and south of these extremities it breaks up into a scattered mass of isolated reefs and islands. The northern portion of the reef proper is more solid than the southern. There are some breaks or gaps in the rampart. These "passages" increase in the southern portion. They occur more frequently and are wider, culminating in the widest of them all, the Capricorn Channel.

The Swain Reefs, an almost uncharted labyrinth of coral shoals, reefs and islets forty or fifty miles wide, are one hundred miles offshore. From here the barrier swings in toward the mainland until opposite Townsville it is only fifty miles away; opposite Cairns, twenty; and off Cape Melville, only ten. A little above that point it veers off again.

Like an iceberg, most of this great coral rampart lies underwater, only a few of the individual reefs becoming exposed at low tide. Nevertheless it forms such an effective protection against the surging fury of the great sea beyond that the water between it and the mainland is often calm as a lagoon and is called Australia's "Grand Canal," a coastal shipping lane.

After their harrowing weeks on the Pacific, when Captain Bligh and his exhausted men began to see terns, driftwood and broken coconut shells, they knew they must be nearing the reefs of Captain Cook's "New Holland." In a few hours they heard the long-drawn, distant roar and soon after saw the line of tossing breakers stretching away as far as they could see, north and south. At last they had reached the Barrier Reef.

Just beyond the furious breakers they could see the placid waters of the Grand Canal. For the nine months of the year when the southeast trade wind blows, the sea pounds savagely on the barrier, giant breakers bursting into skyrockets of spray before boiling over its crest, a-bubble with white foam. Even though the water of the "canal" is only "choppy," when the sea is thundering most furiously on the outer reefs, navigation here is no simple matter. Only experienced pilots can sail the tortuous channels between the maze of shoals, reefs and islands scattered back of the outer reefs. Special pilots known as "Torres Strait Pilots" work the area.

The reef islands are spoken of as "high" and "low." The "high" ones which are nearest the mainland are often described as "wild" or "mysterious" because of their lofty crags, some of which rise thousands of feet and are covered with dense vegetation. The rocky islands were once the peaks of a mainland mountain range. In a long-past geologic age, they were partially submerged when the continental shelf slowly sank into the sea.

Eucalypts, hoop pines, and dozens of other trees cast a mantle of green over their granite shoulders. Sometimes along their rocky shores there are beautiful white beaches, and many of them have fringing reefs of coral. It was on one of these high islands that Captain Bligh landed after finding a safe passage through the reef—and saw a great creature which "ran" by hopping on its hind legs. The botanist with him identified the animal by the name which he said the "Indians" used: "kanguroo."

The "low" islands are true coral islands; or, better, coral cays, to distinguish them from coral atolls. Among the Barrier Reef's myriad islands, there are a few atolls; but the typical ones are cays. The "lagoon" of a cay is simply a kind of moat between the island and its encircling fringe of coral. It shows only as a "lagoon" when the tide is low enough to expose the top of the fringing reef.

The low islands are hardly more than mounds of coral sand covered with dense growths of trees, with dominant types varying from island to island. Among them are tall, brittle Pisonias with mottled gray trunks; Pandanus trees on stilt-like roots and crowned with tufted leaves; and Casuarinas, or beach oaks. There are also dense shrubs and coarse grass. Farther north toward the tropics there are sometimes palms. Here, where the reef swings close to the mainland, there are muddy areas on the lee side of the islands where mangroves flourish.

Lying between the high and low tide mark on many of the coral islands, there are long stretches of the shore composed of solid rock or heaped with slabs of rock called "flatties." This rock, once loose

90

coral sand, has been formed by the cementing action of lime leached from the sand by heavy rains. Downpours, soaking the sand, dissolve the lime. At low tide the rain seeps through the exposed sand; the sun evaporates it, leaving the lime to bind the grains of surface sand into a thin layer.

Layer by layer the loose sand becomes a solid block of rock several feet thick. Tiny fissures appear, the work of waves and rain and sun. They cut deeper and deeper until the slabs fall apart like giant slices of bread; or lie stacked like a deck of cards until a cyclonic wind scatters them over the shore.

Along the east coast of Australia the tide rises and falls twice a day. The spring tides off Townsville range from eight to twelve feet; off Broad Sound the range is thirty feet.

When the tide begins to ebb, the water drains away rapidly; and, as it falls around a coral cay, the moat-like "lagoon" comes into being. Beyond it the receding water reveals a great plateau, drab and uninteresting from a distance. On the seaward side it may be miles wide. The Heron Island reef is a long, east-west oval with the island situated at the western end. Here, at low tide, the edge of the reef is only several hundred yards from the beach. On the east it is so many miles away that the sea is just a blue line between the reef and the sky.

Far away, near the edge of the reef, the monotonous flatness is broken here and there by huge blackened boulders. These are great chunks of coral which once grew on the seaward slope of the reef until, in some storm, the sea tore them loose and hurled them up on the reef. Many of them are encrusted with black lichen.

Between the "lagoon" and the distant black coral-heads, the top of the rampart is studded with pools that glisten like sapphires in the sun. Some are just little basins and pockets from which the water cannot drain, some are much larger, ten to fifty feet wide, from eighty to three hundred long. At the very lowest tides some have only about eighteen inches of water in them, others are much deeper. A long-handled scoop is a useful collecting tool in these deep reef pools.

It is only at a distance that the reef seems drab. Fossickers find it ablaze with color. The literary ones always comment on the huge hermit crabs whose bright red bodies are covered with white or blue spots and bristle with long black hairs; the starfish of neon-light blue; the black sausage-shaped "bêche-de-mer" which the Chinese consider a delicacy in soup; fish gaily bedecked in colorful costumes; many-tentacled anemones strewn about like bright flower heads from a dream world; and softly colored corals looking like the mosses, ferns and small shrubs of a fairyland garden.

Surrounding the pools there are often great storm-wrecked areas and patches of sand strewn with fragments of dead coral. Only the hardier corals can survive on top of the wall where they are exposed to the air twice daily by the falling tide; are at the mercy of hurricane winds and waves; and of torrential rains which are often fatal, for coral cannot live in fresh water. Storms and cyclones play havoc with the reef. The coral garden of today may be "the dust bowl" of the reef tomorrow, a desolated area of dead and dying coral, broken, battered, smothered in sand, or drowned in rain.

The areas of living coral are rainbow-colored. There are chunky brain corals; huge flat ones like rimmed lily pads; delicate flower-like ones growing in clumps and patches like oversized plants of a rock garden.

The character of the coral begins to change near the reef's edge, which is bordered by a rim higher than the rest of the reef. Here coralline algae and encrusting corals creep over the others, binding them into a solid mass, and make the reef look as if buckets and buckets of colored cement had been emptied over it.

The ebbing tide rushes through the deep channels it has cut in the colorful crest of the reef, and pours over the edge in silvery cascades. On all but the calmest days, breakers splash or pound the great buttress. On a rare calm day the lucky reef-comber can peer over the edge and almost straight into the blue abyss. There, growing on the steeply sloping side of the great wall, is an enchanted forest. Unlike those on top, these corals are not constantly subjected to forces of destruction and grow into fern-like "shrubs" and "trees," a stony jungle of fantastic delicacy and brilliant color.

But the shell collector leaves the sunken forest to the spear fishermen and underwater photographers. It is the top of the coral rampart which excites his imagination. The reef at low tide is the shell hunter's heaven.

Fossickers who have written about the reef say that as you wade out on it, you come at once on mollusks. You are surrounded by a riot of color, the brilliant mantles of the clams which are so profuse, one explorer wrote, that if you were to count all you might encounter in the course of one hour's exploration, the number might easily run into the hundreds. Another wrote that they were so abundant that it was impossible to stand anywhere on the reef and not see dozens.

These bivalves are the various species of the genus *Tridacna* whose mantle edges roll back over the deeply scalloped margins of the open shells like great fleshy lips.

The giant, legendary "man-eater," *Tridacna gigas,* inhabits the northern part of the reef. The colors of its velvety mantle, brown or olive green with darker markings and spots of emerald green, are subdued in comparison with those of its smaller relations in the south.

In the northern part of the reef the collector also finds in great abundance burrowing clams *(Tridacna crocea)* and the "bear's paw," or "horseshoe" clams *(Hippopus hippopus)* whose mantles are dull green. The Australian scientist, T. D. Roughley, says that the "horseshoes," like their giant relatives, are never attached, but simply rest, hinge side down, on the bottom.

The smaller burrowing clams, however, are well anchored in the safe pockets they make for themselves. After the early, free-swimming stage of life, the young burrowers settle down in a depression or crack in dead coral or rock and secrete a byssus to hold them securely until they can burrow deep. This they manage to do by rocking back and forth on the hinge until the stone is worn away and they are deeply embedded. No doubt they rock themselves by pressure from the wedge-shaped foot, just as one can rock a chair with a light touch of the toe.

The clams of the southern reef *(Tridacna fossa)* are the most brilliant and beautiful of all. These are the ones which leave the fossickers, seeing them for the first time, in breathless wonder. Their exquisite mantles are matched only by the costumes of the tropical fish. The corals are pale in comparison. There are bright purples, blues and greens mingled with softer browns, fawns and grays. Another reporter adds mauve, yellow and orange to the list, and combinations of all these colors in bands, stripes and mottlings so that no two are alike.

Before the tide falls, fossickers standing quietly can see this brilliant display of mantles through the crystal water; but if they walk across the reef the clams nearby snap shut, squirting jets of water several feet high. If the fossickers pause again, in a few seconds the valves open slowly and the gorgeous mantles creep out. When the valves are wide agape, it is possible to see, in the tissue between the pair of mantles lining the valves, the two circular openings through which the clam sucks in and expels water from which it takes oxygen and food particles. When the tide falls so low that the clams are exposed, the mantles are withdrawn and the valves closed tight.

One fossicker wrote that a mile an hour was a good average speed over the reef because there were so many things to examine and because one had to walk with such care. But that would be much too fast for shell collectors. "To work a reef properly," according to veterans, "you might spend the whole low-tide time working up and down an area about two hundred yards long and one hundred wide. We search for shells *under rocks* as the tide falls and the *sandy places* as the tide makes."

Experienced collectors soon learn that it can be fatal to lose track of time. No matter how engrossed one becomes, it is essential to be a clock-watcher on the reef—essential for safety primarily, but also for successful hunting.

Starting out as the tide begins to ebb, the collector can generally count on two or three hours before being driven home by the incoming tide. Careless collectors have learned to their sorrow that the tide returns as rapidly as it falls, and with it comes peril. It is not a pleasant experience to be caught far out on a reef, loaded with collecting gear and the day's "bag."

"We have learned," one Australian wrote, "that collecting in water deeper than knee-high is best done as the tide falls. Once it has turned and begins to flow, all sea life begins to move, including rays and sharks. If there are troughs to negotiate between sandbanks and reefs, one must be very careful once the tide is running strongly because of the likelihood of encountering sharks headed in from deep-water to the lagoons. One can't depend on their using these passages, however, since sometimes they come right across the reef. We have seen six- and eight-foot sharks literally scrambling through about a foot of water to get into well-filled lagoons which never empty, even at the lowest tides. We had no head-on collisions, just several chilling by-a-hair misses.

"Occasionally deep-sea snakes, all venomous according to one authority, come into reef waters too; and all along the Barrier Reef the conger eels are numerous, large (as long as eight feet!), and very cheeky. They make their homes in the reef pools of untouched islands. They can give a very nasty bite so it is wise to back out of a pool if one appears."

94

Success in hunting, as well as one's safety on the reef, is measured by the hands of the clock. Just as collectors learn that the ebbing and flowing tide has a direct relation to the activities of the dangerous creatures of the sea, they find that mollusks, also, begin to move with the changing tide, leaving their trails in the sand. A bar utterly without trails before low tide will, as soon as the tide begins to ebb, and long before it is noticeable, soon be covered with patterns for the knowing eye to read. Generally, the rarer species will be nearest the low-water mark, and the common species higher up.

Night hunting on reefs is very exciting because the species that stay hidden in the day are on the move then. But, for obvious reasons, night collecting is very risky, far too much so for novices. Experienced collectors plan such expeditions with infinite care, going in groups, never alone, and with many powerful lights, not only to see by but to serve as beacons guiding them back to shore.

Day or night, no one in his right mind allows himself to be left on a reef normally covered at high tide, with only the *promise* of a pick-up by a returning boat. Motors break down, watches stop. Keep the boat with you!

If you are skeptical about the dangers of night collecting on a reef, or being left on one "coming dry," by day, read: "A Walk in the Dark," in Arthur C. Clark's *The Coast of Coral*; and "A Close Call," in *Wonders of the Great Barrier Reef* (see Suggested Reading).

In the first book, four young men walk out on the reef at night to see the living corals, withdrawn by day, emerge from the stony skeletons of their forebears. The men had lanterns to see the "blooming" corals, but none to guide them back to shore.

In the second book, a scientist wanting to photograph corals on an isolated reef, asked a party of friends to put him off while they fished.

Both stories will make your hair stand straight up!

No. 16

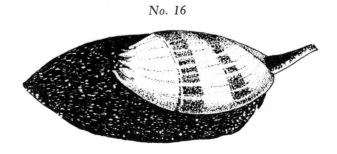

Chapter 17
Handle with Care!
The Dangerous Cone Shells

Dangerous, and often deadly, the dramatically beautiful *Conus* (cone shells) should be handled with great care.

A typical cone shell is broad at the top of the body-whorl and tapers to a narrow base. In some species the sides are not straight, but gently bowed. The spires may be flat, slightly rounded, bluntly pointed, or sharply peaked. Some species are finely sculptured with nodes or delicate beading; most are ornamented with exquisite color patterns. The simplicity of shape, in combination with intricate designs executed in brilliant colors or startling combinations of sub-dued ones, place the cones at, or near, the top of the "want list" of most collectors.

These mollusks are easily first among the species providing ob-servers with dramatic exhibitions if goaded into action or tempted with their preferred foods.

The husband and wife team which collected for the mollusk de-partment of an American museum, were amazed and horrified by the casual way their volunteer helpers in New Caledonia handled poisonous *Conus*. The danger of these shells had been known for years, and the volunteers should have been aware of this danger since they lived on the island and were all ardent collectors. For the sake of science and international good will, they were generously taking the museum collectors to all the best "shelling" spots and assisting in the collecting. After seeing their new friends tuck deadly specimens into tight bathing suits with no concern whatsoever, the Americans decided to stage a demonstration.

The masculine member of the team carefully removed a *Conus textile* from his collecting bag and placed it aperture-up on the deck of the boat from which the whole group operated. He took several puffs on a cigarette, then spat into the aperture of the shell.

Instantly the amazingly long, whip-like proboscis (snout) shot out;

flailed about in an effort to find the tormentor; and, on touching the deck, "fired" its hollow barb. The venom which flowed through it formed a puddle the size of a dime.

"That," the demonstrator said, "is a lethal dose! If the *Conus* had struck any one of you, paralysis would be setting in *now;* and, without medical aid of some sort, you would no doubt be dead in a few hours—and might be, even with aid."

The demonstration had a sobering effect. On the next outing, each of the volunteers was equipped with a newly made collecting bag of sturdy material.

The museum collectors found one New Caledonian who was well aware of the danger of cone shells. She was an elderly Melanesian woman famous for her diving. For many years she made her living diving for *Trochus,* pearl-lined top shells gathered commercially for the manufacture of buttons. At the time the Americans knew her she was envied for her skill in diving for *langoustes,* delectable lobsters of the South Pacific; and had begged a ride to the outer reef in the chartered boat of the collectors.

When she saw the Americans display several *Conus textile* on the deck, she let out a whoop. Backing away from the shells, she cried out in warning, "La guerre! La guerre!"

Though the literal translation means "The war," she probably intended her exclamation to mean "The warriors" or "killers." To the interested Americans she explained, "They show *tents* and have *swords.*"

"Tents" referred to the inverted V-markings on the shell; the "sword" of each *Conus* was the death-dealing proboscis.

All over the Western Pacific, islanders knew of the danger of *Conus* and warned visitors. In 1884, a native of New Britain, acting as interpreter aboard H.M.S. *Diamond,* remarked to an officer who was holding a *Conus geographus,* "Suppose he bite? He kill man."

The officer thought that the man was exaggerating. He could not see how any harm could come from such a creature unless one were to be cut by the lip of the shell, which might result in blood poisoning; yet, thinking there must be some reason for the remark, he questioned the man as to how. His answer was verified by others, one of whom was a white plantation owner. The "bite" might kill.

In 1892, a collector in New Guinea was pleased to find a living *Conus textile* under a rock on a coral reef, but before he could pick it up one of his native companions snatched it away; and "pointing

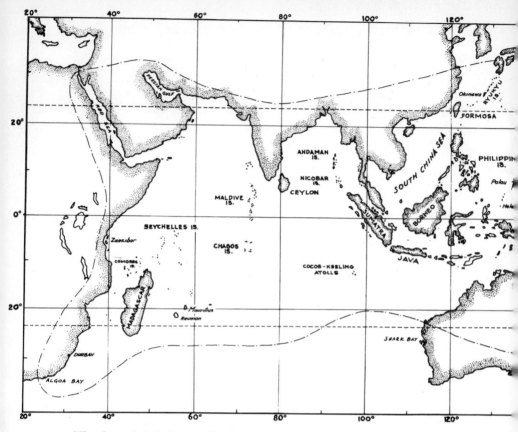

The dot-and-dash line marks the approximate limits of the Indo-Pacific Province on this generalized map of the region.

to its 'business end,' explained with vivid gestures how dangerous the shellfish was." The islander insisted on dropping it himself into the collector's "bottle of spirits."

Writing from the New Hebrides in 1860, a Scotchman who had collected *Conus textile* without mishap in several other places in the Pacific, was surprised to learn that here the "Intrag," as it was called, was very dangerous. Most islanders agreed it was not harmful unless touched, but others said it could "blow" death on one's hand from a distance of several inches. Reasoning that a generally held belief "is never wholly destitute of foundation," he decided that he would handle with caution any live "Intrag" from now on.

After seeing two people who had been "blown on" by "Intrags," both of whom suffered dreadfully and one of whom died, he examined carefully the body of one specimen without discovering any harmful-looking apparatus. No one ever reported puncture or abrasion

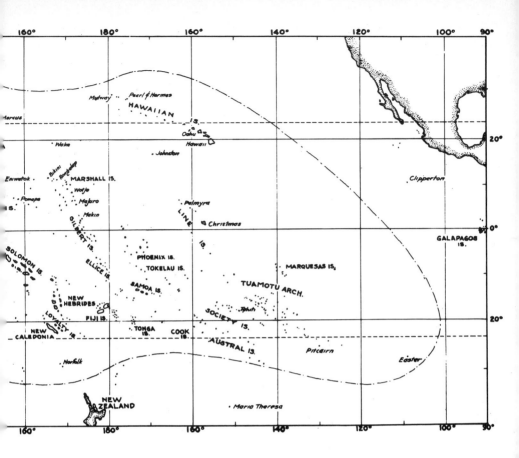

of the skin, only discolored spots. He thought "a jet from the siphon" might explain the impression of being "blown on," but was reluctant to believe that it could be fatal.

Others who had no doubt about the danger of various *Conus*, were also puzzled as to the source of the poison. Perhaps, they thought, it might be the operculum.

The speculations of the earliest reporter came closer to the truth. In 1848, he wrote that he believed the "instrument" which inflicted the wound from a *Conus aulicus* (Courtly Cone) "must have been the tongue which in these mollusks, is long, and armed with two ranges of sharp-pointed teeth."

The poison "dart," a characteristic feature of the Conidae (cone family), is a modified radula tooth. With this group of mollusks, the radula tooth is no longer a rasping cusp on a ribbon-like tongue, but a hollow needle with a barb at the tip and a knob at the opposite

The hollow radula tooth of the deadly harpooner, Conus striatus (Striated Cone), showing the barbed tip and knobbed end. Greatly enlarged.

Conus striatus *with the proboscis extended. External organs labeled.*

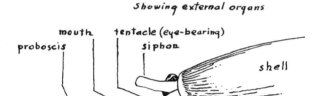

end. A supply of these teeth is kept in a sac in the head of the snail. The poison is in another sac. A tooth travels from its sac through the proboscis to the tip, where it lies ready for use. When the snail "strikes," the hollow tooth is jabbed into the victim and the poison flows through it. In some species the tooth is shot free like an arrow; in others it is like a harpoon, being held fast by circular muscles at the tip of the proboscis which contract around the knobbed end.

The auger shells *(Terebra)* possess a similar apparatus, but there are no records of injury to human beings attributed to these "cousins" of the cones.

Bites or stings of *Conus* have been described by victims as causing "sharp" pain, like that of a wasp sting, or "great" pain. One man who died five hours after having been stung in the palm of his hand, is reported to have suffered no pain.

Published reports describe other reactions like these: immediate stiffness, swiftly spreading numbness, blurred vision, creeping paralysis, soaring temperatures, rapid shallow, or "difficult" breathing, coma.

For many years only six out of about four hundred species were known to be venomous:

Conus aulicus—Courtly Cone
Conus geographus—Geography Cone
Conus marmoreus—Marbled Cone (now called *monile*)
Conus striatus—Striated Cone
Conus textile—Textile Cone
Conus tulipa—Tulip Cone

Recent reports have added these to the list:

Conus imperialis—Imperial Cone
Conus lividus—Livid Cone
Conus nanus—a subspecies of *musicus*
Conus obscurus—Obscure Cone
Conus pennaceus—Pennaceus Cone (formerly called *omaria*)
Conus pulicarius (Handsome Cone)

Some of these may be rated as "deadly" because of numerous, well-documented cases of fatalities caused by their stings; other are merely "dangerous" because the injuries inflicted by them, though painful, were not fatal. Some might have been so if the victims had not had prompt medical attention.

For example, the eight-year-old girl on New Guinea who collapsed after being stung on the palm of her hand by a *Conus pennaceus* was rushed to the hospital where she was given artificial respiration and injections of Vitamin B_1 and penicillin. Two hours later she regained consciousness, but the treatment was continued for two more hours. By the next day she was completely recovered and no aftereffects were reported.

Of those species listed, one authority, who has done extensive research on *Conus,* considers *Conus geographus* as the most dangerous to human beings, perhaps because of its size. A six-inch *geographus* probably injects twice as much venom as a species like *tulipa* whose maximum length does not exceed three inches.

Yet size is not necessarily an indication of dangerousness. This authority does not consider the huge *Conus leopardus,* which attains a length of nine inches, a menace to collectors because its stinging mechanism is poorly developed.

Apparently this species does not have to kill its prey before eating. The primary purpose of the stinging action is to secure food, paralyzing it so that it may be devoured with ease. The secondary purpose is self-defense.

Conus are not considered aggressive animals. When disturbed, they shrink into their shells and stay there. An observer hoping to see the snail emerge, generally has a long wait, unless he provokes or lures the creature into action.

Although many a venomous *Conus* has been collected without harming the collector, again and again the documented accounts of injury or death from a *Conus* sting say that the person was struck as he reached in the water. One was collecting by moonlight and picking up things he could not see well!

It is reasonably safe to pick up a specimen provided the collector is careful—and care, to judge from these experiences and from recent research, would suggest not only being able to *see* what you are about to pick up, but rolling the shell over with a gadget so that the animal will withdraw; and then approaching it from the *rear*, as one would do to pick up a crab or lobster to avoid the snapping claws.

Once picked up, the specimen should be put immediately into a container or a sturdy collecting bag which is not in contact with the collector's body. Cones have been known to sting through mesh bags. They should never be held in the hand, put in a pocket, tucked in a bathing suit or sarong.

In case after case of fatal or near-fatal attacks, the medical reports say the victim was stung in "the thenar region," the base of the thumb. The man who died in five hours after being stung, was holding his specimen in his left hand while scraping away encrustations on the shell with a penknife. The New Guinea girl, stung in the hand also, may have been admiring her pretty discovery.

An experienced collector, who knew better but had grown careless, put in the back pocket of her heavy overalls four *Conus*—*textile, catus, rattus* and *nussatella,* collected during a camping trip on an isolated island which was part of the Great Barrier Reef. One of *Conus* stung her.

"Since our launch had returned to the mainland seventy-five miles away," she wrote, "and we had no other means of communication, the situation could have been serious. Fortunately it was not. We

102

had a first-aid kit, and my husband treated the sting as one does a snake bite. Except for persistent soreness over a period of five weeks, there were no ill effects."

Evidently the offender was not the *Conus textile,* and the other three species should be added to the suspect list.

With this close call uppermost in her mind, she impressed the mission girls who helped her with collecting on New Guinea with the need for caution.

"The girls were great shellers. They went out neck-deep on sandy bottoms; felt around with their toes; brought one foot up backwards and passed over to us a nice *Conus. That's* the way to shell!

"We warned them, of course, of a possible sting but felt there was no danger in letting them collect in that way as long as they were quick about it; and that we did stress. We gave explicit orders that they were to be *quick* in picking up the specimens with their toes; and in passing them back to us. We wanted no *Conus* tucked in their lap-laps!"

Recent observations of Hawaiian *Conus* show that with some species, two of which are widely dispersed over the Indo-Pacific region, quickness in handling and care in subsequent disposal are precautions which might be as futile as locking the barn after the horse has been stolen. At certain times, feeling around in the sand for these species is tantamount to kicking at a coiled rattlesnake. In his study of Hawaiian *Conus,* Dr. Alan J. Kohn found that both *Conus striatus* and *Conus catus* frequently lie as ready to strike as a coiled snake, and the motivation is neither annoyance nor fear, but hunger.

All *Conus* are believed to be carnivorous predators, but they don't all eat the same animals. The range of their food preferences is wide.

It had been known for some time that certain species feed on dead fish. To learn that two, and perhaps three, species are capable of successfully attacking *living* fishes was headline news in the scientific world. Inasmuch as the announcement came from a well-qualified professional malacologist, the report on his observations would have been accepted by scholars without question. His report, however, was supported by indisputable evidence: moving pictures of a snail attacking and devouring a fish.

Conus striatus, found throughout the Indo-Pacific Province, was chosen as the star. It lives on sandy bottoms in the shallow water of reef platforms and also in deeper water; and feeds on small bottom-

Feeding process of Conus striatus (*Striated Cone*)

1 and 2. Proboscis (*snout*) is extended toward the fish.

3. Proboscis is in contact with the fish.

4. The fish is stung and impaled on the ejected radula
tooth. The photograph is
blurred because of the thrash-
ing-about of the fish.
5. The fish is drawn into the
distended buccal cavity.

6. All but the tail has been
swallowed.
7. Engulfment is complete.

swimming fishes like blennies, and others, which swim higher, but make forays to the bottom.

The specimen placed in the aquarium for the movie-shooting buried itself in the sand with only the tip of the siphon protruding. Within seconds after a blenny had been put into the tank, the *Conus* became alert. The foot stirred, raising the snail to the surface; the proboscis stretched out and began to "track" the fish as it swam past. Although it came within a few millimeters of the proboscis, "cocked" with a poison dart, the *Conus* did not aim and fire as a gunner would; but waited until the unsuspecting fish actually brushed the tip of the sinuous snout. At that instant the snail shot its venomous dart; but the lethal tooth was not freed like an arrow. The knob at the rear was firmly held by the muscular tip of the proboscis. *Conus striatus* harpoons its prey.

The poison flowing through the hollow dart quickly paralyzed the fish. When it ceased struggling, the snail retracted the proboscis, drawing the impaled victim toward its mouth which, like that of a snake, expanded enough to swallow the fish whole!

This species, as well as *Conus catus,* also under intensive observation and found to feed essentially in the same manner, are able to engulf fishes as large as themselves, and sometimes larger. They do not gulp their victims; the swallowing takes time. As the contracting proboscis *pulls* the fish into the larger portion of the snout, the muscles there *push* the fish along the passage until it is completely inside. For several hours the distended snout remains engorged. The fish has to be partially digested there, before it can be passed on to less expandable parts of the alimentary tract (see pages 104–105).

Dr. Kohn found in observing his specimens that the *Conus* venom acts more quickly on some kinds of fishes than it does on others. If the wounded fish manages to tear itself free of the barbed dart, and this does happen, the snail retracts the proboscis and then "spits out" the dart; otherwise the tooth goes down with the fish. The spitting out is a slow process, lasting from ten to thirty minutes. When darts missed their targets this same process followed, leading the observer to conclude that each dart is used only once. If, for whatever reason, the shot is not successful, the dart is ejected and a new one from the radula sac moves into place at the tip of the proboscis, and the *Conus* is ready to strike again.

In an effort to find out how the snails become aware of the presence of an exciting meal several experiments were tried. At the

106

start of each test the snail was buried under the sand, with only the siphon visible.

There was no reaction when the water of the aquarium was stirred with a glass rod, nor when a dead fish was dropped near the *Conus*, even though the fish was a species readily eaten when alive. When water from a tank of living fishes was poured into the test aquarium, the snail responded immediately, emerging from the sand just as it had when a live fish was put in the aquarium. This seems to suggest that neither sight nor movement evoke response; and that the initial stimulus is probably chemical.

The transmitter is the *osphradium* (ŏs-frā′dĭ-ŭm), a chemo-receptory organ found in most aquatic mollusks, but more highly developed in the Conidae than any other family. In its passage through the mantle cavity, the stream of water drawn in by the extended siphon passes over the gill and *osphradium*. The name is derived from a Greek word meaning "strong scent."

When living fishes were put into the aquarium, the emerging snails never failed to be ready for the kinds offered them. By some means they knew just how to aim their snouts. When bottom-swimming fishes like blennies were the prey, the proboscis was held just above the sand surface. With the introduction of others, the proboscis was held vertically. The "reach" of the proboscis is about half the length of the shell. A specimen approximately four and a quarter inches long (115 millimeters) can extend the proboscis approximately two and a quarter inches (60 mm.).

Just suppose the groping toes of the New Guinea girls had touched one of the fish-eating species with the loaded proboscis extended well beyond the shell!

These observations had not been published when the Australian collector was out with the New Guinea girls. From now on, no collector in his right mind will "feel around" blindly for any *Conus*. Future research may show that other species lie, as *Conus striatus* and *catus* often do, ready to strike. The *Conus pulicarius* (Handsome Cone) which stung a Hawaiian collector was partially buried in the sand.

A great many species of *Conus* live entirely on marine worms and each species appears to have its own favorite or favorites, thus enabling as many as eleven Hawaiian species to co-exist peacefully in a restricted reef area. This theory was tested on two species of *Conus* and two species of worms whose distribution on the fringing reef

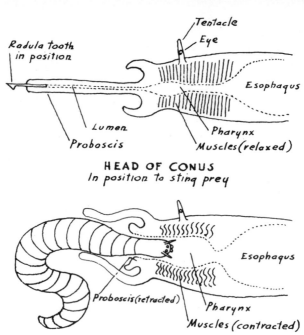

Radula tooth
in position

Tentacle

Eye

Esophagus

Lumen

Proboscis

Pharynx

Muscles(relaxed)

HEAD OF CONUS
In position to sting prey

Esophagus

Proboscis(retracted)

Pharynx

Muscles (contracted)

HEAD OF CONUS
In process of feeding on a worm.

overlap. Each *Conus,* repeatedly offered both kinds of worms, invariably chose the "right" species, the one it had seemed to prefer. Thus competition between closely related species living side by side is reduced. Among the species feeding on marine worms, some are "harpooners," some "arrow-shooters." In either case, the fatal dart is swallowed along with the meal it supplied. Since the worms, like the fishes, are so much larger than the snout in its normal condition, it must expand as the prey is pulled in.

Occasionally worms are eaten without being stung. The huge *Conus leopardus* simply extends its orange *rostrum,* the larger portion of a telescoping snout; pushes it against the worm; and begins to suck it in by muscular contractions. The proboscis with its dart was not seen and apparently never used. The great size of this *Conus,* with the weakly developed dart-shooting mechanism, may explain this method of eating; however, other species, known to use darts, sometimes ate some victims without stinging them first.

When a *Conus lividus* and a worm were put in a pan of sea water together, the *Conus* extended the rostrum, but not the dart-tipped proboscis. When the mouth, the opening at the tip of the rostrum, touched the worm, it opened and closed on its prey. The

108

worm, apparently unaware that it was being swallowed alive, kept up its normal pulsations until it disappeared from sight!

Conus generally do their feeding at night, and one worm a night makes a meal. This conclusion was reached by the dissection of many specimens collected at various times of day and night.

Beside the fish- and worm-eaters, there are three species of *Conus* which have very different tastes. *Conus pennaceus* and *Conus textile* feed entirely on other marine snails; and the feeding process is essentially the same. Both species shoot the dart free.

Whereas one poison dart is sufficient to kill the prey of the species feeding on marine worms, it often takes as many as six darts to kill the prey of these two species feeding on other snails. Victims with internal shells are engulfed like the fish and worms, the shells being regurgitated later, it is thought. Victims with large external shells are not swallowed.

After striking its prey, each of the *Conus pennaceus* under observation applied its mouth to the aperture of the prey's shell and began to suck. As soon as fifteen minutes later, or as long as an hour later, the empty shell fell away from the mouth of the *Conus*. It is thought that during this time the venom loosens the one muscle attached to the shell so that the "body" can be pulled out easily and swallowed by the attacker.

In the aquarium *Conus textile* attacked and ate three other kinds of *Conus;* two kinds of *Cypraea* (cowries); one each of *Turbo, Thais* and *Drupa*. Two other *Conus* may be added to this varied menu. A *Conus textile* found on the reef was still swollen with the soft parts of a *Conus striatus;* and inside another, which was dissected, the operators found the radula sac and operculum of a *Conus pennaceus*.

Conus pennaceus, however, though eating a wide variety of snails also, will never touch other cones; and *Conus marmoreus,* apparently, will eat nothing but other cones!

Most marine creatures must be aware that it is foolhardy to try to dine upon *Conus*. Although it happens so rarely that it can be considered negligible, adult *Conus* are preyed on occasionally. The attackers are thought to be parrot fishes, zebra eels, and some starfishes. In the test aquarium some crabs attacked, but succeeded only in breaking the lips of the *Conus* shells. The mollusks were able to retreat far enough into the shells not to be harmed.

Under the circumstances, it comes as quite a surprise to learn that one intrepid attacker was another marine snail: *Cymatium nico-*

baricum (Golden-mouth Triton) one of the smaller species of *Cymatium*.

When put in aquariums, it attacked venomous cones without hesitation. Once a specimen crawled up to a *Conus ebraeus* (Hebrew Cone), boldly thrust its proboscis into the aperture, and evidently began rasping bits of the living cone's unprotected foot with the radula. The operculum in the Conidae is not nearly as large as the aperture and cannot seal off the withdrawn snail from predators.

How strange that with first rending of flesh the *Conus* did not fight back! If there had been an attempt to emerge and strike or run, the observers would surely have reported it.

The *Cymatium's* meal was indeed a leisurely one. It lasted nine days!

In their marine world it is likely that the deadly *Conus* have met their match in the *Cymatium*. It is interesting to compare the reports on *Conus* by other observers with those of Dr. Kohn.

Three people who had collected many specimens of *Conus regius* (Crown Cone) and *Conus mus* (Mouse Cone) on an outer reef of the Florida Keys, put them in white enamel trays of sea water and teased them with probes, hoping to incite them to strike. All but one specimen ignored the provocative poking. Suddenly one of the inch-long *Conus mus* extended its fleshy proboscis from the tip of which the fascinated observers saw the "sharp brown needle" emerging. The snail then raised the proboscis high in the air before jabbing it down on the *shell* of another *mus*. A thick, milky-white fluid spurted from the hollow "needle," forming a cloudy spot in the water a quarter of an inch in diameter, before disintegrating.

On picking up a large *Conus spurius atlantics* (Alphabet Cone) from a Florida west coast mud flat, one of a party of four collectors found that the proboscis was buried in the mud. As the collector lifted the specimen, the whitish, fleshy tube stretched and stretched and stretched! The length was so astounding that two of the others compared it with their arms, while the fourth photographed the procedure. The length was about thirty inches. Suddenly the tip came free of the mud and much of the fleshy tube contracted quickly into the shell. The rest remained in view.

It did not seem possible that the proboscis could have been so long. The collectors concluded that part of the long tube was a marine worm which the *Conus* was in the process of swallowing. They could not, however, distinguish any difference in color or texture, nor could they see where the two were joined. The moment was not appropriate for, nor conducive to, careful observations. No one had a magnifying glass; an icy wind was blowing; and the tide was already creeping back over the flat which was proving to be a fine collecting spot.

At the end of the day, that specimen was placed in a basin of water and next morning the collectors noticed an unattached, fleshy, worm-like object in the basin by the snail. My husband and I were two of the four collectors, but unfortunately the specimen was not ours. Had it been, we would have sent it and the worm-like object to our professional friends at Harvard's Museum of Comparative Zoology. We suggested that the owners might do so, but evidently they did not.

The skilled husband and wife who collect for the American museum reported that of the several species of *Conus* collected in the Palau Islands, only two could be induced to attack victims for the benefit of the eager audience composed of less experienced members of this large expedition and the crew of the expedition's schooner, *Gloria Maris*.

The stage managers were very disappointed that the famous "killers" of human beings, *Conus striatus*, *Conus tulipa*, and *Conus geographus*, could not be made to perform in the aquarium. *Conus marmoreus* was the most retiring of all. It retreated into its shell and stayed there.

Conus auratus and *Conus textile* were more obliging. In fresh sea water these crawled about actively. When replaced quickly in water after being held aperture-up so that fresh water or saliva could be dripped on any one of the retracted snails, a brilliant red proboscis, evenly tapered from base to tip, shot out and explored the surroundings with a sinuous movement. The "reach" of a two-inch specimen was about one and a half inches.

Numerous "victims" were thrown to these gladiators. Neither *Oliva* nor *Nassarius* interested them; *Cypraea* (cowries) did.

As the waving proboscis came in contact with a *Cypraea*, an immediate heightening of excitement was evident. After testing several locations, the proboscis tip pressed against the chosen spot. A quick spasm followed, the proboscis becoming swollen and rigid for a moment. Although pressure was being exerted, the proboscis was more curved than straight. At the moment of the strike, a milky cloud appeared at the tip of the proboscis. The organ was withdrawn immediately with some of the milky fluid still flowing from it.

111

Several times the watchers saw the small "glass-like barb," which the attacker had plunged into the victim's body.

Sometimes it took two strikes to kill small species. Large ones, like *Cypraea tigris,* although obviously affected, continued to live. After the strike, the attacker seemed to lose interest in the victim.

Once when several small *Conus textile* were placed in a container with a crawling four-inch *Conus geographus,* a *textile* one-third the size of the large *Conus* crawled alongside promptly and stung it. A second *textile* followed suit; and within five minutes the *geographus,* most dangerous to human beings, was limp and apparently dead.

There are several possibilities that may explain the lack of interest that the Palau Island specimens showed after attacking or killing the prey given to them. The first is a full crop. If collected in the early morning, they were probably still digesting the meal of the night before. Dr. Kohn's specimens fed at night even in the lighted laboratory. The Palau Island *Conus textile* were stimulated enough by the desirable prey to kill them but not hungry enough to eat them.

The second possibility is that after attacking the *Cypraea,* the *Conus* decided to roam around while waiting for the poison to take effect and loosen the prey's body from the shell, instead of waiting patiently with mouth pressed to the aperture as *Conus textile* and the other mollusk-eaters did in the laboratory. Perhaps prudence made them crawl away from the big *geographus.*

The third possibility is that the Palau Island collectors had neither the time nor equipment, a mechanically aerated aquarium, to continue their observations long enough to see what might have happened. With a busy collecting program, they no doubt had to give up watching and water-changing for collecting and processing. As far as they went, however, the observations of these collectors suggest an even wider range in the catholic tastes of *Conus textile.*

And if they had tempted their *Conus marmoreus* and *Conus striatus* with a greater choice of food, they might not have found them "most retiring."

The *marmoreus* might have bestirred itself for another cone; and if a blenny had been thrown to the *striatus,* it might have given them a real show.

Most *Conus* are found in warm tropical waters, and the Indo-Pacific Province has the largest share of species. There are some fifty species native to the Americas, many of which are exceptionally beautiful, some extremely rare. None of these is *known* to be venomous, but it is prudent to handle all species with caution. On the general assumption that if venomous, the degree of pain or danger to life will be in proportion to size, the larger specimens should be handled with very great care.

Once your specimens are safely collected, keep them alive as long as you can in whatever you can muster as an aquarium; offer them a choice of food—and see for yourself what happens.

No. 17

Chapter 18
A Common Family of
Uncommon Interest: *Crown Shells*

Judged by appearance, shells in the family Melongenidae (crown shells) deserve high rank. In this respect they are aristocrats of the back bays, the preferred habitat of many species. Rated by rarity, they would come near the bottom of the list.

Yet for those not prejudiced against them because they are common and easily obtained, a comprehensive collection of the species in this family would make a stunning addition to any collection. All the branches of the family are very handsome; and, in some groups, there are remarkable variations. The reasons for these geographic and ecological variations are fascinating.

These snails are popularly called "Crown Shells" or "King's Crowns," because of the thorny "coronet" ornamenting the shouldered whorls of most of them. The scientific name *Melongena* is derived from the Greek words *melon* (apple) and *genos* (kind). The name is also translated as "eggplant." The shells are similar in shape to that vegetable; and also in color, in some species, if the protective outer coat is removed.

All of the American members of the family of crown shells belong to a subdivision (subgenus) called *Rexmela*. *Rex* means *king*. Along the west coast of Florida, collectors will find an amazing diversity of forms (see page 115). Colonies only a short distance apart may be quite dissimilar. Within some colonies, most individuals may be as alike as soldiers in uniform; in others, as different as endless combinations and variations of the basic features can make them.

There are specimens with a single row of spines at the shoulder, others with two or three. On some, the spines flare out; on others, they point up, or curve in. Some specimens are almost white, others dark with thread-like spiral lines of white. Between the two extremes, there are infinite combinations of wide and narrow bands of brown, gold and white. Adult specimens range in length from two to eight

Melongena corona *(Crown Shells)*

inches. Yet all are classified as *Melongena corona corona*. Why? Thoughtful investigators wondered.

Marine species whose young have a long *veliger* or free-swimming stage, generally develop in one of two ways. They are uniform throughout the area of distribution; or else they show a graded change, or *cline*, from one end to the other of their range. There are, of course, exceptions. The type of variation found in the west coast *Melongena corona* seemed to indicate to professional investigators that some factor in their life cycle prevented wide dispersal of the young. A study of specimens kept in an aquarium proved this to be true. All stages of the development of *Melongena corona*—egg, trochophore, and veliger larvae—are passed within the egg case, or capsule. When the escape pore of the capsule ruptures, a tiny, crawling snail emerges; and, barring some accident like floating away on a piece of driftwood or branch of mangrove, it will live out its life in a restricted area (see page 116).

The hands of time, however, have shuffled those colonies thoroughly. In the millions of years that they have been on this coast, as we know from fossil forms, they have had to adjust themselves repeatedly to changing conditions. As the land mass sank, or sea level rose, they found themselves in deeper water than they were accustomed to; and, to re-establish themselves in the intertidal zone, they had to migrate to newly submerged areas. Where individuals with a similar gene complex chanced to congregate, the succeeding generations continued to be uniform; where individuals from different colonies were mixed in a new assemblage, a varied population evolved.

With the next geologic upheaval, this process was repeated in reverse. The survivors were those individuals which followed the retreating waters, re-grouping in the littoral zone of the new geologic age.

All of this region is so low that even minor changes in the level of the sea would affect great areas of the coast. The area where the greatest mixture seems to have occurred is between Tampa Bay and Cape Sable.

At each end of the *Melongena corona* range, there is a distinctive subspecies. *Melongena corona altispira* (high-spired) extends from Cape Sable, at the tip of the peninsula, east and north nearly to St. Augustine. The specimens generally found throughout the range are smaller than the typical *Melongena corona*; and, if they have shoulder spines at all, they are not well developed. Usually there is no row of spines at the base. *Melongena corona altispina* does not appear to be abundant anywhere in its range.

The author holds a living Melongena corona johnstonei *(Johnstone's Crown Shell). Note the curling-in edges of the snail's foot as it withdraws; and the nearly horizontal edge of the operculum (trapdoor) just above the upper edge of the foot. To the left is the tongue of a water-soaked shoe to which a female has attached eleven egg cases. The "escape hatch" which will rupture to allow the baby snails to emerge is at the top of each case.*

Fig. 2

Fig. 1

Fig. 3

Melongena corona johnstonei (*Johnstone's Crown Shell*) *Compare this sub-species with that shown on page 115. Figures 1 and 2 have not been cleaned. Figure 3 has. Note the operculum in the aperture just below the catalog number. These specimens are in the Mollusk Department of the Museum of Comparative Zoology. Fig. 1 is the* Holotype, *the single specimen chosen as "the type" by the "authors," the malacologists, Drs. Clench and Turner, who described the subspecies. Figures 2 and 3 are* Paratypes, *"side types," as all the other specimens examined in a study of this kind are called.*

The other subspecies, Melongena corona johnstonei, is considered a fine example of a smooth cline, an orderly progression of change, from the area where it merges with the typical form of *Melongena corona* to the end of the known range in the lagoon at Gulf Shores, Alabama. As he moves westward, the collector finds specimens increasing in size and becoming more slender in proportion to the width, and less spiny.

The curious cannot but wonder how it is that *Melongena* from adjacent coasts developed so differently. Why is it that the specimens on the North Gulf coast are uniform in appearance, and those around the bend on Florida's west coast so diverse? How did the colonies along the North Gulf coast escape the shuffling to which those of the Florida west coast were subjected?

Again, malacologists look to the past for an explanation. The fossil record is too incomplete at present to give a positive answer; but it suggests that, if *Melongena corona* was established on the North

117

Melongena melongena—*West Indian Crown.*

Gulf coast during the warm Pliocene, it must have been killed during the cold period of the Pleistocene which followed; and, later, when it was warm again, new individuals reached this coast and established colonies. Storm tides or winds must have brought them on driftwood beyond the tidal flow just north of Cedar Key, which separates the typical *Melongena corona* from the subspecies *johnstonei.* Isolated from the parent stock, the newcomers developed uniformly.

The remaining species found in the United States is the beautiful, tobacco-brown and white dwarf *Melongena bicolor,* of the Florida Keys. Whereas others in the family prefer the brackish water of back bays and lagoons, this species was reported as living only on the ocean side of the Keys on beaches where marl and sand are mixed. But people who have specialized in collecting *Melongena,* searching the coast intensively for them, have discovered four colonies on the Florida Bay side of the Keys. Beaches peppered with *Cerithium* and *Batillaria* (horn shells) are likely places to hunt for this pretty miniature species, because these very small snails seem to be favorite food of *Melongena bicolor.*

This completes the list of native "crowns." Across the Gulf of Mexico there lives what is thought to be a stranded relative. The Double-Spined Crown (*Melongena bispinosa*) is known only from Yucatan. This species may be a surviving remnant of a group which,

Melongena patula—*Pacific Coast species.*

in warm Pliocene times, was widely distributed. As the glaciers slid down from the north in the frigid Pleistocene, plants died and animals died or moved south. The Yucatan *Melongena* is considered a *relict,* "left behind," species, cut off from the other surviving members of this big family. It resembles some of the forms of the High-Spired Crown Shell of the east coast of Florida.

The West Indian Crown Shell and its Gulf of California offshoot look much more like an eggplant in shape than our native crown shells, both of the former having rounded "shoulders." The "crown" of the West Indian species (*Melongena melongena*) is usually formed of double, occasionally triple, rows of sturdy, thorn-like spines. A single row spirals around the base of the shell. All the islands cannot claim this species; only Cuba and its Isle of Pines, Jamaica, Hispaniola (Haiti and the Dominican Republic), and some off the coast of South America. Its continental range extends from Dutch Guiana to Tampico, Mexico (see page 118).

In a past geologic age when the land-bridge connecting North and South America was submerged, it is possible that the West Indian species ventured into the Pacific as adults or as egg cases floating on debris, and, with the rising of the Isthmus of Panama, was cut off. Developing in isolation, it became so differentiated that it is now considered a distinct species. This crown shell, *Melongena patula*

(Gaping-Mouth Melongena), grows to much larger size than specimens of parent stock, and is much darker. Like the parent, some of these may have no coronet of spines; those that do, have but a single row (see page 119).

The species found from Trinidad south around the bulge of Brazil belongs to another family group, *Pugilina*, and is of interest for two reasons. First, it is one of a few species found on the east, as well as the west, side of the Atlantic; second, like the West Indian and Gaping-Mouth species, many individuals are "uncrowned." According to a 1950 report, the range of this species on the Atlantic coast of Africa extends from Cap Blanc (on the bulge of Africa north of Dakar) to some way south of the mouth of the Congo.

The earliest known specimen was one of these without a coronet. It came from Gorée Island, Sénégal, and was described by the famous Swedish naturalist, Carl Linnaeus, in the tenth edition of his epoch-making "Systema Naturae." Linnaeus classified the shell as a "rock-shell" or *Murex,* calling it *Murex morio.* The spiny form was described later by the French naturalist Lamarck. He grouped it with the spindle shells, *Fusinus,* but gave it the specific name *coronatus.* Today it is classed as one of the crown shell family, Melongenidae, and is called *Pugilina morio* (see page 122).

There appears to be no popular name for this species. Perhaps it is just as well. The Latin name won't frighten away veteran collectors; and novices who aspire to being serious collectors will want to learn to use scientific rather than common names. This is a good one to start with for it is not a jawbreaker.

Both crowned and uncrowned *Pugilina* may occur in the same locality. A long series of specimens will show a complete intergradation of the two forms.

The Brazilian collector from whom we received the first specimen in our collection, wrote on the data card: "Mangrove coast. Sand-mud bottom. Uncommon in this area." In an accompanying letter he said: "If you care to remove the periostracum, you will find the shell is a rich, dark color, almost purple."

A second specimen from Trinidad provided another locality for this species. Both specimens were left in their natural state. The shell color, a brownish-purple banded with white, can be seen in the enameled aperture.

Some species in this family offer interesting opportunities for discoveries. All the ground has not been covered by the professionals; there are many areas not reported on at all. Collectors stimulated by the thought of exploring new territory have work cut out for them.

At present there is not enough scientific information on two members of this family. Scientists would welcome an intensive search by serious amateurs along the Florida portion of the east coast inland waterway and the Indian "river" area for the High-Spired Crown (*Melongena corona altispira*). They would welcome gift specimens if accompanied by accurate locality data (see Chapter 21).

The Yucatan crown *(bispinosa)* has been collected only at Progresso and Dzilam de Bravo. Collectors who wished to make a contribution to science, could search for, and no doubt find, this species in other localities along this coast. So little collecting has been done there, it offers a real challenge to enterprising hunters.

The subspecies *johnstonei* has a very limited range, as far as is known. It begins about where the west coast of Florida bends to the west and ends in the lagoon at Gulf Shores, Alabama. If this species continues along the coasts of Mississippi, Louisiana, and Texas, it has yet to be discovered. A few collectors have searched some of this coast, but their efforts were not successful.

On the other side of the world a veteran collector had a rare experience in a wild, little known part of the northwestern coast of Australia. On a hard mud shore bordered with mangroves, she discovered a colony of living snails which were unfamiliar. She collected forty specimens and sent them to the National Museum of Victoria for identification and was excited to learn from the Curator of Molluscs, J. Hope Macpherson, that the shells appeared to be a new species. In a 1958 publication they were described by the curator as a new species of *Pugilina* named for the finder, Elizabeth Grigg—*Pugilina griggiana*—who had given some of the specimens to the Museum collection.

Perhaps in a similar habitat on other unexplored shores, other new species await discovery.

Keen observation, records, and reports are just as important as the discovery of known species in new places, or species which may prove to be new.

Dr. Ruth D. Turner wrote me: "I hope you will stress the necessity and value of observations on all living mollusks. For example, there is not enough known about any species of *Melongena*. We should like to know:

> When they breed.
> How long the development takes.
> Where they lay their eggs or put their egg capsules.
> What they eat.
> How long they live.
> How fast they grow.
> How far they travel in a day.

"And so on, and so on."

What a challenge to young marine scientists, and to older people with the leisure to pursue a new interest intensively and make a contribution to science!

Outgrow the beginner's preoccupation with the "rare" and "exotic." Forget the Aphrodites of the deep; seek and know the Cinderellas of the shore.

No. 18

Chapter 19
Stop, Look—and Learn!

The most vivid description is surpassed by one good look. Even the briefest glance, at the right moment, may be more revealing than pages of words. Observation is routine procedure for professional malacologists and their students. For many serious amateurs, it is a fascinating part of their interest in shells, a wonderful way of learning.

Collectors who live by the sea, or who can afford (and master the balancing of!) a salt-water aquarium, are especially lucky because of their great opportunities for extended observation; but average collectors whose time is limited to vacations are not handicapped as much as you might think. In even a few minutes on a sand flat, or by a tide pool or a makeshift aquarium, they can learn more by watching than in hours of study.

Until you see with your own eyes the mantle lining a snail shell, slipping back and forth as the snail retreats or emerges; until you see in the species having a siphon that it is a rolled extension of this lining; until you see one kind of snail turn a "somersault" and another track its prey with its snout; the most accurate description gives only a hazy impression. Descriptions are useful, however, in arousing initial interest in observation; in indicating what to watch for; and in explaining or clarifying what you see.

Any non-metallic container will do for an aquarium if refilled often enough with fresh sea water. Some specimens may be kept alive for days. A pyrex baking dish served as our first aquarium for the pretty little *Nerita peloronta* (Bleeding Tooth) (see page 138) which we found on coral rocks in the Florida Keys. An enameled basin was the "ring" in which the clown-like *Strombus pugilis alatus* (Florida Fighting Conch) delighted us by turning somersaults when placed on its "back," and by seeming to peep at us between tricks from under its shell with long-stalked eyes. Each eye was protected by one up-curved tentacle, like a single eyelash.

One of two Cypraea cervus (*Atlantic Deer Cowries*) *which we kept alive to observe. Note the foot, the bulbous eyestalks, the eye on the left bulb, the tapering tentacles. The tip of the lifted tentacle is directly in front of the partly extended siphon. The mantle lobes meet on the top of the hump, but part just above the siphon. The "warts" studding the lobes would expand greatly under water. See photo of the same species below.*

A living Cypraea cervus (*Atlantic Deer Cowry*) *photographed in an aquarium with the mantle, its protuberances, the eyestalks and siphon fully extended. Note the lifted edge on the side of the foot. This specimen was collected in the same locality as the one shown on the author's hand. Marine biologist Robert C. Work, of The Institute of Marine Science, University of Miami, reports great color variations in this species. There are specimens with an all-black mantle, like the one shown here; others with a gray mantle; some with mottled gray and white, like that of the author's specimen; and some with a black-and-white mantle.*

A pair of *Cypraea cervus* (Atlantic Deer Cowries) (see page 124) lived happily for a week in a glass-bottom "spongers'" bucket, giving us ample opportunity to observe them from below as well as from above. These so-called "shy" creatures proved not to be shy at all. They performed beautifully for us and a circle of fascinated sunbathers on the beach who gathered around to watch also. Removed from the water-filled bucket, each cowry in its turn withdrew completely through the slot-like aperture into the shell; but when placed upside down on my palm, immediately righted itself by stretching out its pad-like foot far enough to touch my hand and pull the shell over. We watched the lobes of the mantle slide up the shell until they nearly met on the domed top; and then the creature glided up my wet arm. The mantle lobes were studded with little wart-like bumps which would have expanded and looked like the long, pointed protuberances in the specimen on page 124 (bottom) if the captured specimens had been in their own environment and undisturbed.

The protuberances on the mantle of *Cypraea zebra* (Measled Cowry), (facing page 130), look torn or tattered. The specimen is "facing" you, so that you look directly into the siphon. The golden-buff of the shell shows between the edges of the mantle.

The foot of each of the three species of cowry shells which we have collected, *Cypraea zebra*, *Cypraea cervus*, and *Cypraea cinerea* (Measled, Deer, and Gray Cowries), has been like a gently rounded mound. In photographs we have seen of several other species the foot of each appeared to be similar. It may be that when the need arises, cowries can elevate the foot considerably and swivel the shell. We have seen two species of *Fascilaria* (Tulip Shells), *tulipa* and *hunteria*, do this often. Even so, I do not believe the foot of the cowries we have observed would have looked in the least like the steeply sloped, deeply ruffled feet of *Cypraea tigris* and *Ovula oviformis*, now called *ovum* (Tiger and Egg Cowries) on pages 126–127).

It is possible, however, that these drawings may not be "true to life." It seems reasonable to believe that many of the anatomical drawings of shells published in books a century or more ago may have been inaccurate. They were made by naturalists, their students, and interested amateurs who had the distinction of being the first Europeans to collect in the seven seas in the sixteenth, seventeenth and eighteenth centuries. Their field sketches were then redrawn for European publications by artists who had never seen the living mollusks.

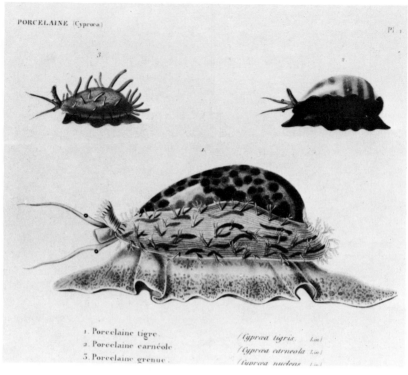

1. Porcelaine tigre.   *Cypræa tigris.*
2. Porcelaine carnéole   *Cypræa carneola*
3. Porcelaine grenue.   *Cypræa nucleus*

Compare the sawtooth edge of the siphon of Fig. 1, Cypraea tigris, with that of the black Cypraea cervus (Atlantic Deer Cowry) on page 124. Notice the difference of the fleshy protuberances on the mantles in this plate and on those shown on other plates.

There may have been notations by the sketches made in the field like: "The foot undulates," or: "The foot appears to ripple as the creature crawls." The collector, who may have had no talent for drawing, and the artist working from amateurish sketches and sketchy notes, did their best to show the foot in motion by drawing ripples at the edge.

These drawings of cowries appeared in a now famous set of books published between 1837–1880 by Kiener and Fischer: *Species General et Iconographie des Coquilles Vivantes* (Common Species and Illustrations of Living Shells). Compare these drawings with photographs of living cowries (*Cypraea*) shown in this book and in many of the books in the list of recommended reading.

Some of the best performers in makeshift aquariums are the various species in the big family of shells called this or that kind of

126

"moon shell" or "shark's eye," Naticidae . Many species are easily found on flats in shallow water around the world.

These mollusks are noted for their ability to plow under the surface of sand or mud with a foot designed for this purpose. It becomes tremendously distended for plowing, but can shrink enough to withdraw completely into the shell, sealed tightly with a beautiful operculum.

We have often watched with fascination *Polinices duplicatus*, the moon shell of our Atlantic and Gulf coasts, called Shark's Eye; and we have learned to have only shallow sand in our basin because, if the sand is deep enough, this arch burrower is out of sight in a matter of seconds. In sand less than half an inch deep, specimens will slide around and around searching hopefully for a deeper spot and, while doing so, give observers a good chance to see another interesting feature. From the front portion of the foot (the *propodium*), a lobe of flesh rises and creeps up over the shell, actually bending the tentacles backward. A similar extension rises from the rear of the foot (the *metapodium*), so that only the very top of the shell

The foot and mantle of this species, Ovula ovum, are velvety black; the protuberances are creamy white. The white shell is the size of a goose egg. Because of the color of the interior, rich brown to yellow, the shell is popularly called the Poached Egg Shell. Although it looks very much like a cowry it belongs to another family: Ovulidae.

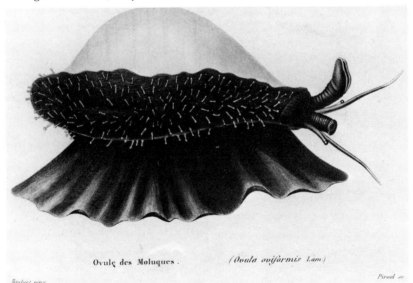

Ovule des Moluques .   *(Ovula oviformis Lam)*

Baubert pinx   *Piroel sc*

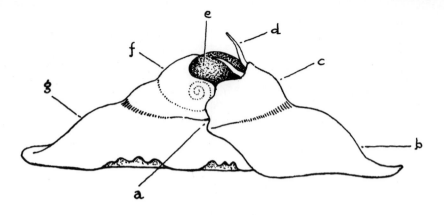

Natica josephina. *Animal fully extended.*
a = *exhalent orifice*
b = *propodium, front part of the foot*
d = *tentacles, bent back*
c = *part of the propodium reflected on the shell*
e = *shell*
f = *posterior part of the foot reflected on the shell*
g = *metopodium, rear portion of the foot*

can be seen. The front lobe is an asset to the sand-burrowers, but it is not designed for the protection of eyes, because many of the species traveling under the surface are without eyes (see above).

The pad-like foot of gliding snails may be divided lengthwise or crosswise by a muscular ridge or furrow; and sometimes the two sections move alternately. In those where the division is lengthwise, the animals sway from side to side as they progress. When the division is across the foot, the front portion moves forward first and is followed by the rear portion, so that· the creeping of these snails resembles the movement of caterpillars. A gland in the foot secretes mucus to help the gliders. Try looking through a glass surface at the underside of your specimen's foot.

Some snails have a beautifully ruffled foot. These are species which live on a very soft bottom and the foot is modified to slide, or coast over the surface. Broadly expanded in all directions, the foot serves the snail like a snowshoe.

If you should be lucky enough to find a Rose-Petal Bubble Shell (*Hydatina physis*)—and you may because this species is found in many places around the world—you will see a foot like ruffled flower petals, pale blue touched with beige. The round shell, white with fine brown lines, is like the "eye" of this flowerlike animal.*

A frilly foot is characteristic of many members of this family. The ruffles in front grow long like rippling rabbit ears, from which comes the popular name "sea hares." Below there are shorter extensions. Both sets are head tentacles. Collectors in south Florida and the West Indies could find an equally beautiful bubble shell, *Hydatina vesicaria* (Brown-lined Bubble); and collectors in Hawaii and throughout the Indo-Pacific Province should watch out for a pink-and-white banded bubble shell, *Amplustrum amplustre* (Amplustre Bubble).

The "leaping" snails are fine candidates for makeshift aquariums. Many of them are easily collected in shallow water. The best known are the members of the strombid family, Strombidae. Familiar American species are the Fighting Conchs *Strombus pugilis, Strombus pugilis alatus;* and the great Pink or Queen Conch, *Strombus gigas* (the "chowder" conch). They have relatives all over the world. These snails have a narrow, compressed foot with a scythe-shaped operculum at the rear. Strombids move jerkily, hitching the shell forward; and, when placed on their "backs," easily flip themselves over. This is the famous "somersault."

Although the foot of Florida's *Fasciolaria hunteria* (Banded Tulip Shell) is pad-like, it becomes compressed when the shell is placed upside down, and lashes out vigorously in an effort to find something to jab the pointed operculum in, and flip the shell over. This species rivals the various *Strombus* in performing this feat.

By all means watch your specimens in makeshift aquariums; and, if you are able to visit some of the great aquariums of the world, allow plenty of time for mollusk watching. Sometimes great battles take place in mollusk tanks.

But above all learn to watch for action when you are out collecting. Sometimes there is plenty of it.

Out to see what he could see on an Atlantic coast sand flat at low tide, a student witnessed a scene which proved that the rapacious *Polinices duplicatus* (Shark's Eye) has more than one way of killing its victims. The well-known method is drilling a hole with its file-like "tongue" (radula) through the shell of a hapless bivalve or a snail held firmly in the huge, muscular foot of the

* There is a color photograph of this beautiful snail, in *The Great Barrier Reef* (see bibliography), Plate 73.

Polinices. With the hole finished, the predator thrusts its long snout (proboscis) into the soft part of its victim and dines at leisure.

A number of times the student had found a *Polinices* feasting on a slime-coated *Ensis directus,* a razor clam. The proboscis was inserted *between* the valves, *not* through a hole in one valve. How, he wondered, had the snail been able to catch this species renowned for its ability to "leap" and burrow with speed? One day he had the good fortune to see a battle from beginning to end.

He found a clam on the surface, its foot writhing, a snail attached to the lower portion of the shell. After some moments, the clam freed itself and managed to burrow into the sand. The snail burrowed in beside it and evidently attached itself to the lower part of the clam. The clam's effort to escape carried it up to the surface where it lay writhing again, with the snail hanging on doggedly. The process was repeated a number of times, the clam growing weaker with each one. After the last burrowing, there was no more activity. The observer dug up both specimens and watched for thirty minutes longer. The clam showed no sign of life. Its whole body was coated with slime secreted by the snail's foot. The student concluded that the secretion must act as an anesthetic—like the purple "dye" of the Purple Sea Snails dining on the little Jack-Sail-by-the-Winds.

Cowries are so beautiful, both the shells and their mantles, and their life habits so interesting, that some collectors along Australia's Great Barrier Reef, which is famous for its many shells, are known as "cowry watchers." They specialize in watching "sitting" cowries. They observe carefully, takes notes, and report their findings to scientists.

The female *Cypraea* sits on her eggs just as a hen does, and is said to protect the jelly-like cluster with the lobes of her mantle. Since breeding habits of *Cypraea* and allied groups are most irregular, watchers cannot be sure of success at any particular time, but this only adds zest to the hunt. One set of watchers reported that, over a period of years, in an area where there were twenty species, they found only one sitting. Then in October of one year they were rewarded in finding another species sitting; and two months later, two more species. A watcher from another part of the Great Barrier Reef reported a scarcity of *Cypraea* in her area for a year; then, after late June, many appeared and began to "nest."

The watchers also report on the colors of the *Cypraea* (cowries) and their eggs. A group of three enthusiasts from Queensland saw

Cypraea zebra (Living Measled Cowry); mantle expanded, covering most of shell, tentacle and eye at lower right. William M. Stephens

one species sitting on bright yellow eggs. A watcher from the south reported that the mantle of this species harmonizes with the eggs. It is gray with yellow dots. Some individuals in this species have darker-than-normal shells, and these, watchers report, lay correspondingly dark eggs.

One of the great Melon or Bailer Shells, *Melo amphora* (see page 95) common on the reef flats, held particular fascination for an Australian who spent as much of his time observing as collecting. Whenever he found them, he could not resist following the tracks of this large snail. To be sure, he knew that more often than not he would find a handsome shell, valuable in exchange for other species, buried at the end of the trail, but he did not follow the tracks just to pick up the prizes. Once he was doubly rewarded. He dug out of the sand hill at the end of the track a fifteen-inch female, which was feasting on her six-inch mate. Having heard reports of this practice, he was pleased to see it with his own eyes.

As an experiment he gathered six or eight *Melo* egg cases in various stages of development and put them in a rocky "pen," which he made, hoping to see the hatching of the baby snails.

He described the cases as "semi-transparent, like celluloid." Other observers describe them as "glistening." They may be yellow or white and are shaped like a corncob with individual capsules arranged irregularly around a hollow core, through which the fully developed baby snails eventually emerge. The average size of the "cob" is about two inches in diameter and nine or ten inches in length, but the Australian *Melo*-watcher reported that he had seen some as long as eighteen inches.

A violent storm wrecked his experiment by destroying his artificial pool and washing away all the cobs. Later, however, he was more fortunate. In a protected natural pool, he found a *Melo* just beginning to make its egg case, which was anchored securely to a loose stone, and he was able to watch the whole process from the start to the hatching of some two hundred small *Melos* about three months later.

The Americans who were collecting in New Caledonia for the museum had wonderful luck one day when they were swimming off a shoreline reef in about seven feet of water. In five different places, they saw colorful circles like the heads of giant daisies lying on the white sand. On closer inspection, they found that the pale yellow "petals" were *Conus quercinus* (Oak Cone) and that the pink "eye" of each was a gelatinous mass of egg capsules. In each group there were from twenty to thirty individuals "facing" the pink center with their siphons raised like the trunks of trumpeting elephants.

"Hating to do it," wrote the record-keeping member of the team, "but trying to be scientific in our approach, we bagged one entire 'nest,' the shells and the beautiful egg mass. Back on the boat, still excited by our discovery and wanting to share it with the others, we arranged the egg mass and shells just as we had found them. As we watched we had an added thrill. One of the yellow *Conus* added a glistening pink egg capsule to the clump of others."

On a sandy reef flat in the Indo-Pacific Province, another "watching" collector came across a sight so strange that he published an account of it. A popular account might have been titled "The Shell with Walking Eyes," but this description appeared in a scientific paper as: "Observations on the Gastropod *Terebellum terebellum* (Linnaeus), with particular reference to the behavior of the eyes during burrowing."

Terebellum terebellum belongs to the great family Strombidae, but it is not shaped at all like the best-known members with their flaring shells. It is designed for a life of burrowing just under the surface of the sand. The shell is bullet-shaped, smooth as china, and prettily patterned with red-brown dots or stripes or a combination of dots and stripes.

The animal burrows so rapidly that its movement is described as "darting." It can change direction by rolling sideways with agility. It has a long, narrow foot, a large snout between two long eyestalks each of which is tipped with a blue eye, and a short eyelash-like tentacle. Growing from the front portion of the mantle there is a *"siphonal appendage,"* a fleshy flap which becomes a tube when the edges are drawn together.

As the snail crawls under the sand it leaves one blue eye on the surface, behind it, not dragged along, but stationary. The long stalk grows longer.

When the eyestalk has stretched as far as it can, about an inch, the siphon-fold is thrust up through the sand and parted to allow a current of water to be sucked into the mantle cavity. Then the siphon-fold closes, forming a tube; and up through the tube comes the second eyestalk. When the eye surfaces, the protective sheath

132

Terebellum digs into the sand and travels forward, keeping one or the other of its eyeballs at the surface at all times. (Hypothetical drawing based on an account by D. P. Abbott, 1962, and based upon anatomical studies of the authors, Peter Jung and R. Tucker Abbott.)

unrolls and is withdrawn. At the same moment the first eye, well to the rear, is also withdrawn—and the process starts all over.

The watcher saw this eye-walking repeated over and over again by several snails. He compared the exposed eye to a periscope.

While you watch for action, keep an eye out for beauty. It is there, too.

Seeing is believing. Until you see for yourself the textures, colors, and patterns of molluscan "bodies," it is hard to believe that many are as beautiful as some birds or butterflies. "Bodies" is not the correct term. Scientists speak of "the soft parts," because the shell is as much a part of a mollusk's body as your bones are of yours.

I always carry a strong magnifying glass on collecting trips and spend hours looking at my catch; and making notes and sketches in my field book. For example:

Little Knobby Scallop *(Chlamys imbricata)* moderately common.

Mantle-fringe: blue-black tipped with yellow.

Tentacles edging the mantle: cream.

Eyes embedded in mantle edge: glittering dots of gold.

Shell: exterior white, sculptured like the famous "Lion's Paw."

Interior enameled with lavender and lemon.

On the Great Barrier reef of Australia, a small white cowry creeps about on a crimson foot, and cloaks its granulated shell with a red mantle studded with miniature "staghorns."

In the warm Atlantic waters of our side of the world, the three *Cyphoma* (Flamingo Tongues)—*gibbosum, mcgintyi,* and *signatum* —seem by general agreement to be the beauty queens because of their lovely mantles.

In my opinion they have stiff competition. One rival is the lavender, spindle-shaped *Neosimnia acicularis* (West Indian Simnia) with its mantle of lavender overlaid with a net-like pattern of

133

magenta, tufted with tiny golden "staghorns." The other is the jewel-like *Prunum carneum* (Orange Marginella). The polished, brilliant orange-red, bean-size shell is wrapped in a mantle of the same luminous shade which is sprinkled with white polka dots; and it glides about on a foot finely striped with this vivid color and white.

Beauty and drama await the "watcher." Learn by looking!

No. 19

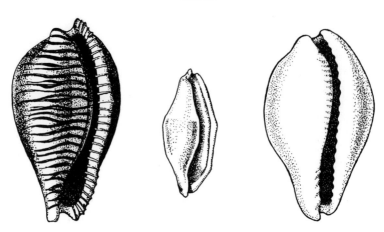

Chapter 20
Conservation

It is the collector in shallow water on whom the great responsibility of conservation rests. He must be conscientious enough *to take time* to turn back the rocks he has overturned; to discipline himself in the number of specimens he collects. He should never clean out a colony; he should never collect by the bushel basket when he is fortunate enough to come on great numbers of mollusks at any time, and especially when they are in the shallows for breeding.

It is dismaying to hear that anyone considers it "unreasonable" to expect collectors to replace rocks. The fact that many do so is ascribed to a selfish desire to continue to have good collecting in that spot. What if the collector knows he may not return for years—or ever? Most professionals and serious laymen urge and practice replacing rocks as a matter of principle. Failure to do so is wanton destruction, of which no one with fine sensibilities would be guilty. One does not ruin a marine habitat any more than one sets fire to fields and forests, collector or not; and conscientious collectors feel an obligation to those who will follow them.

Two forceful paragraphs on conservation appear in *Sea Shells of Tropical West America* (page 6) and *Between Pacific Tides* (page 11). The authors of the latter say that anyone who doubts the necessity for such care should examine a familiar intertidal area after it has been combed by a biology class which has failed to replace rocks. At first the spot simply looks disarranged, out of order, like a ransacked room; later it is desolate, littered with forms of life that have died because of exposure or wave action. With the living conditions disrupted, Dr. A. Myra Keen points out in the first-named volume, the delicate balance between hosts of plants and animals which keeps an area productive, is upset. We are reminded by the other authors that it will take weeks or months for such a spot to recover.

A number of states protect edible and commercially valuable species by requiring a fishing or collecting license, and placing restrictions on the number and sizes of mollusks to be taken; but the inedible species need protection also unless our coasts are to be stripped by thoughtless amateurs and greedy commercial collectors.

Some areas are overcollected because they are widely known and easy to reach. "The few times I've been to our good spot lately," a collector in Florida wrote, "I have had very poor luck. Too many people know about it now. In spite of all, many good things are still taken there, but not as often as before."

Even distance does not save some places famous for fine shelling. In a later letter the same person wrote of a reef seven miles at sea: "The hump was barren; it looked as if it had been thoroughly worked over. However, under one rock I found five or six *Conus regius* (Crown Cone) building an egg mass, and moved them, along with their eggs and rock, to deeper water where there would be less chance of their being discovered."

Do not overcollect. Take only the best, and what you know you can care for. It is very distressing to move into a vacation cottage and find the ground around it littered with shells collected alive which the former occupants didn't bother to clean—or return to the water.

Since it is our habit to keep a number of specimens alive for as long as possible, we are able to weed out as we go. On the first day of a recent vacation on one of the Bahama out-islands, we found seven *Cassis tuberosa* (King Helmets), but we took only the three best back to our cottage. We put all we found in our boat, but when the time came to go we picked out the three with the best color and least encrustation and left the rest in their home spot. We kept the good ones alive in a sack, weighted down and tied to a post, in the water under the wharf. As the days went by, we added the best of the others we found. Leaving ourselves just time to clean and pack them, we chose the best four of those in the sack and put the rest back in the ocean where there were others of their kind.

To be sure, this species is a handsome one and is not available near home. It is nice to have extra specimens to give away or to use for exchanging, but you have to remember others feel the same way. If every collector takes every specimen he finds of the especially desirable species, then before long . . .

I won't finish the sentence. I'll quote a news item which appeared in our local paper in July, 1968.

Fig. 1

Fig. 2

Fig. 3

Charonia variegata *(Fig. 1 and 2) Atlantic Triton*
Charonia tritonis, *Fig. 3, Pacific Triton*
There is a close relationship between these two species. The colors—white and many shades of brown from pale beige to chocolate—are similar, but there is a difference in size. The Atlantic species ranges from 8 to 13½ inches in length; the Pacific from 8 to 15 inches.
The most obvious difference is seen in the outer lip. The lip of the Pacific species flares out and the "teeth" (plicae) are flatter or indicated only by color markings. The teeth of the Atlantic species are usually short, paired, white ridges set in a chocolate spot. Note in the two species the difference between the teeth and the amount of dark color on the inner lips. Note also the short siphonal canal of each.
As you see, the first whorls of the embryonic shell shown here are quite different from those developing later. This difference is characteristic of all the species, more than a hundred, in this large family: Cymatiidae. The Atlantic species is found in the Mediterranean as well as on both sides of the Atlantic Ocean, generally about rock reefs below low water. Little is known about the feeding habits of most species. It is thought that they are probably predatory, feeding mainly on other mollusks.

137

Reef Life Upset by Shell Collectors

Melbourne—Australia's Great Barrier Reef, a 1,000-mile living coral construction, is being destroyed by starfish that thrive in the absence of their natural enemy, the triton mollusk. The mollusk shells have been raided by collectors, upsetting the reef's ecology.

The "triton mollusk," *Charonia tritonis* (see page 137) in that area, is also a large, handsome shell. Individual collectors like extras; souvenir shops and commercial dealers like to keep well stocked. As a result of thoughtless greed you see what is happening in an area a thousand miles long, and a mile wide in some parts.

Don't be selfish; don't be stupid.

Set a limit to your "take."

Because a rich area, even a seemingly inexhaustible one on a tropical coast, can be ruined by overcollecting if news of it travels too far and fast, only general areas are described in this book, never specific localities. But there is a second reason for this: the supreme pleasure comes in making your own discoveries.

No. 20

Chapter 21
Record-Keeping

Record-keeping is an important part of shell collecting; and simplicity is the key to doing a good job. If the method of recording the essential information about your shells is too complicated it takes the fun out of collecting, and amateurs won't bother with this step.

The monetary, as well as the scientific, value of a collection depends far more on the information in your catalogue, than on the perfection or rarity of the specimens. Specimens without reliable information about where, when, and by whom they were collected are of no scientific value whatsoever. A private collection made up of specimens without this basic information does not interest serious amateurs or institutions, and could not be sold to such purchasers if the need arose. Material of this kind given or willed to a scientific institution would be discarded, no matter how beautiful, perfect, or rare the specimens might be.

This basic information is called "locality data."

The one absolutely essential piece of information about a shell is *where* it was found. This was not true in the early years of shell collecting.

The first, and now famous European collections of the eighteenth and nineteenth centuries, were filled with "mystery" shells: shells from heaven-only-knew where. Some of the collectors were students sent out by the early scientists to roam the world; others were ship captains or their crews who gathered and sold shells and other "curiosities" to rich people for the fashionable "cabinets of curiosities" of that time. Sometimes the collectors found the shells themselves; sometimes they obtained them from fishermen who may have gotten them from far away. Collectors may have guessed where the shells came from if the buyers were curious; and they often guessed wrong.

Scientists of that day were not really bothered by not knowing where a shell came from. For them the name was all important. The name was, and is today, the key to how the shell is classified. Each

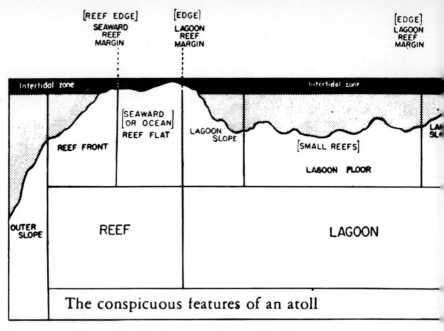

The conspicuous features of an atoll

Cross section of a coral atoll showing reef terminology.*

scientist decided by the *look* of a specimen whether it was a *Murex* (rock shell), a *Fusinus* (spindle shell), a *Cassis* (helmet) or a *Cypraea* (cowry). There were no soft parts to dissect and compare with drawings of dissected parts made by other scientists. After deciding what genus in what family the shell belonged to, the scientist then gave the shell a second name which would distinguish it from all others in the family or group in the family to which he thought it belonged: red, golden, spotted, rugged, spiny, crowned.

Scientists often published catalogs for private collectors, or books, with beautiful hand-colored, wood-block printed illustrations. Many specimens were shown with no information about where they came from. If another collector wanted such a shell he had no idea where to look or send for it.

In time such shells became known as "lost." Just a few years ago several "lost" shells were found in the Gulf of Mexico by commercial fishermen working off Yucatan, Mexico. An example is the Turnip Whelk *(Busycon coarctatum)*. The first specimen belonged to an English earl and appeared in the illustrated catalog of his

* For those interested in recording detailed information on mollusks collected on coral reefs and atolls, we recommend the reef terminology employed by Joan Demond. The editor, R. Tucker Abbott. From *Indo-Pacific Mollusca.* Courtesy of The Academy of Natural Sciences, Philadelphia.

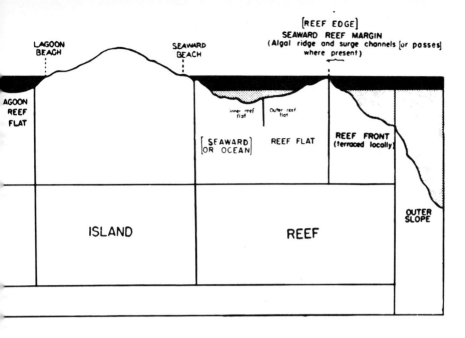

LAGOON BEACH

SEAWARD BEACH

[REEF EDGE]
SEAWARD REEF MARGIN
(Algal ridge and surge channels [or posses]
where present)

LAGOON REEF FLAT

inner reef flat   outer reef flat

[SEAWARD] OR OCEAN   REEF FLAT

REEF FRONT (terraced locally)

ISLAND

REEF

OUTER SLOPE

collection in 1825. In later publications, its origin was guessed at: "The coast of Florida?"—"West Florida?"

At present the name of a shell is the least important information about it. The name can be changed a dozen times and often is, as opinions about its classification change, or for some other reason. The information about its origin never changes. Geographic origin is important because the range over which the shell occurs is based on the places where collected.

What is considered good locality data?

1. Geographic locality. (To within less than a mile from a fixed landmark.)

The names of countries or states alone are not adequate. It is important to know *where* in China or Chile, California or Connecticut. Even adding the city name is not enough. The location should be given as accurately as possible with relation to some permanent landmark: "ocean side, half a mile east of old Fort Royal"; "from lagoon one mile west of lighthouse"—or "off main dock at Kingston Harbor."

2. Depth of water. (Intertidal or beyond.)

3. Type of bottom. (Rock, sand, mud, grass, coral.)

4. Date. (Might indicate a phase in life cycle.)

5. Collector's name. (Often a matter of interest. Also, frequently an indication of reliability of the record.)

141

6. Dead or alive. This information is especially important with rare species.

These details give a clear picture of the kind of place the shell lived—its habitat. This much information is considered good, a satisfactory minimum, but why stop there when so much more is needed and, in many cases, could be given? Why not give more than just enough?

Professional malacologists constantly remind amateur friends that there is so little reliable information about the living habits and life cycles of even the most common species that every scrap which can be contributed is important. Scientific training is not necessary for most of this; just knowledge of what information is valuable, and willingness to take time to observe and record it.

7. Additional information of value is:
- a. Relation of shell to bottom: on top, buried, attached to.
- b. Type of water: quiet or turbulent; hot or cold; clear or murky.
- c. Living habits: solitary or with others; a day or night mover; breeding season; appearance of egg masses; food; method of feeding; enemies; any special behavior.

These are examples of such reporting:

Virgin Islands—"One *Conus* to a sand hill, barely covered."

Ceylon—"*Fusinus* (spindles) were feeding on *Thais* (rock shells) which were feeding on *Mytilus* (mussels).

Great Barrier Reef—"*Haliotis scalaris* (Staircase or Three-ribbed Abalone) lives just below water under loose slabs of stone or attached to them, well camouflaged by weeds of the shells' color. They would be easily missed if they did not move off rapidly when the stone is lifted and sometimes shed a portion of the foot."

This process, you remember, is called au-tot′o-my; and it means self-division.

"And all of this must be written for each kind of shell? Too much work!"

Good news. You write it only once, at collecting time, in your notebook for "Field Notes."

Field notes are work records and may be terse. Even so, to beginners they may seem like time-takers. Actually they are time-savers.

Each collecting spot or "station" is given a number. For example, in the diary excerpts, three stations were described. They were

142

Harry Inge Johnstone prepares to photograph living specimens at a motel in the Florida Keys. Photography is a most important part of the record and a contribution which many amateurs can make.

numbered 1, 2, and 3 in the field notes for the New Providence trip, August, 1957. Trips to an outer reef and an offshore island were stations 4 and 5.

The locality data for each station is jotted down in a few words: geographic location with relation to a fixed landmark, date, name of collector or collectors, type of bottom, depth of water. Note the other information suggested for superior data, if you wish.

List the species about which you wish to make a comment concerning interesting living habits, behavior, or appearance. Nearly all the interesting things in this book about the living conditions, actions, and appearance of various shells have come from some collector's field notes.

For your own future use it is helpful to list *all* the species found at a station. If you found many good shells, your record will remind

Busycon contrarium (*Lightning Whelk*)
Two views of the same specimen laying an egg case.

you that it was an excellent spot to which you might like to return. If you found nothing much, you'd cross it off as not worth another visit.

If you don't know the scientific names at the time of making the record, list the common ones.

12 keyhole limpets
10 chitons
2 big helmet shells
3 hawkwing conchs
1 colorful moon shell with red and white foot.

Later, when the shells are identified, you can add the Latin names.

It is really very simple.

Only the station number is written on a card which is enclosed with each day's bag of shells. When they are sorted—some set aside for observation in a makeshift aquarium; some plunked immediately into a preservative; some cleaned, dried, wrapped in paper, and packed—only the station number is packed with them or taped to each container they are in. The station number stays with each specimen, or batch of specimens, until the final cleaning is done.

When the shells are ready for cataloging, all the necessary information about the place they came from can be found by the corresponding number of the Field Notes. The shells may or may not be identified at all or correctly. Proper identification can come any time. Get a number on the shell and the proper information about the shell recorded in your catalog.

With good record-keeping you are well on the way to being a "serious amateur."

No. 21

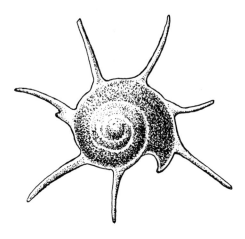

Chapter 22
Cleaning and Curing

The choice of methods used for cleaning shells will depend on the number you have, their sizes and kinds; the facilities at hand, and the time.

There are four safe and easy methods, feasible for vacations or collecting near home. "Easy" is a relative term. If there are large numbers of shells and many sizable ones, cleaning is going to be quite a task. There are many steps and, with several kinds of shells which have to be treated differently for success, the job can be very tedious indeed.

During the various stages of cleaning you should keep each operculum, "trapdoor," with the shell to which it belongs; and you should also keep the number of the collecting station with each shell, or batch of shells. Depending on the cleaning method, your specimens will be in plastic pill vials, glass jars of various sizes, or plastic freezer boxes.

To avoid becoming hopelessly discouraged or ruining what you have been lucky enough to find, inexperienced collectors should not burden themselves with too many shells. Keep only the best, then do your best to do a good job of cleaning.

The safest and easiest cleaning methods are: soaking in an alcohol solution, freezing, boiling, and hanging.

SOAKING IN ALCOHOL

The great advantage of this method is that it is safe and a time-saver on vacations or field trips. The shells, washed of grit and mud, may be put into the solution in glass jars with screw tops and forgotten until there is time for further cleaning. They may be brought home in the jars if the collecting is done in your own country. Sending specimens from one country to another in alcohol, in metal containers, is too much of an undertaking for inexperienced amateurs.

The longer the shells soak, the easier it is to remove the soft parts which have been loosened at the point of attachment. They must soak for at least three days; and may soak for months with no damage to the shells.

If many shells from different localities are to be put in the same container, they should be kept separate. Put them in lightweight cotton bags. The top of the bag does not have to be hemmed for a drawstring. Stitching on the sides and bottom is enough. The top may be tied with string or a strip of cloth. Many small specimens of different kinds may go in one bag, *so long as they are from the same locality*. Larger specimens may require a bag for each.

Put the proper station number in each bag. Ordinary paper will not do for these labels because it disintegrates in alcohol. Use identification tabs of heavy, smooth cardboard with which orchid fanciers and nurserymen tag their plants. They are about four inches long, a third of an inch wide, and come in several colors. White ones are best. Use a No. 2 lead pencil for writing the station number. Crayon and grease pencil numbers dissolve in alcohol.

Bivalves

The bivalves will have opened and the major part of the flesh can be flushed or pushed out. Gently scrub out the rest, rinse, and dry. If there is a byssus, save it. Rinse and dry it, too; and put it by or in your specimen in several folds of tissue paper. After thorough drying of the shell, apply mineral oil to the ligament, and decide whether you want the specimen flat out, like a mounted butterfly; open to whatever degree is natural; or closed. If the specimen is to be closed, bind it with thread or string. If it is to be flat, the hinge has to be broken.

Snails

Some collectors kill their snails by leaving them out of water overnight, or in fresh water. This is to prevent the sudden contraction of the snail when dropped in alcohol. If the contraction is immediate and the operculum a close-fitting one, the alcohol may be sealed out completely, or to such an extent that the soft parts decompose.

147

Small specimens

After they are removed from the solution and dried, very small snails need no further cleaning. The odor goes away in time and the operculum of each shell is in place without the nuisance of pulling or picking the flesh out; and replacing the operculum in a fold of tissue paper, or stuck to a bit of cotton.

Larger specimens

The soft parts must be removed. The tool for this may be any strong pointed object: a big safety pin opened out, a hat pin, a knitting or crochet needle, a dental tool, ice pick, or meat skewer. The choice depends on the size of the shell.

1. Hold the shell firmly by the body whorl (the last and largest turn of the shell) taking care not to press on the outer lip if it is thin.

2. Note the position of the operculum so that it may be placed correctly if you plan to put it back, stuck to a bit of cotton.

3. Insert the pointed implement in the thick part of the foot just back of the operculum. If there is a siphonal canal, slide the instrument up or beside it.

4. With a steady pressure, *roll* the soft part out. Once the muscle attached to the columella (spiral core) breaks loose, the rest should slip out easily. Sometimes, however, the very soft part coiled in the spire breaks off. Sometimes this part can be shaken out or flushed out with a jet of water. If it can't, another step is necessary.

Some species are much harder to clean successfully than others because of the shape and size of the aperture; or the size of the muscular attachment and its place, near the aperture or deep within a tightly spiraled shell. Success comes with experience. The efficacy of the soaking-in-alcohol method was impressed on me when I saw the soft parts which had been removed from a five-inch *Turritella*, (turret shell). The delicate corkscrew was perfect from the tip, which had fitted into the spire of the shell, to the foot with the attached operculum. This part, preserved in a vial of full strength rubbing alcohol, was stored with the shell.

5. When the soft part comes out intact, cut or pull off the operculum, wash and dry it.

6. Rinse the shell thoroughly, scrubbing away or wiping out with a cotton-tipped stick any scum left on it. Set the shell aside with the operculum by, or under, it to dry.

148

7. When the shell and operculum are dry, wrap the operculum in crumpled tissue paper or a wad of cotton and stuff it into the aperture of the shell. Later, after further cleaning, if this is what you want, the operculum may be glued to a wad of cotton and replaced in the shell so that it appears as it did when the shell was alive. At this point the specimen is clean and ready to be cataloged.

Throughout each of these steps with each specimen the slip of paper with the station number has moved along with the shell, or should have.

If pure alcohol is available, use a seventy per cent solution of it (70% alcohol and 30% water). In the United States ordinary "rubbing" alcohol is a seventy per cent solution; and is a reliable substitute for expensive, hard-to-come-by pure alcohol, cut with water. Use it right out of the bottle. This will serve also for indefinite preservation of soft parts removed from shells.

Packing alcohol-soaked specimens

If there is not time to complete the cleaning of specimens through the removal of the soft parts, and if the trip home is not a long one, the snails may be packed after soaking for as long as possible in seventy per cent alcohol.

Drain the specimens well. Wad cotton or tissue in the apertures of all but the very small shells. Put each specimen in a plastic bag (take a supply with you if you go to an out-of-the-way place); and wrap well in crumpled newspaper. Pack snugly into a cardboard carton or zippered canvas carryall, putting the largest and heaviest specimens on the bottom. Fill all the spaces with more crumpled paper so that there can't be any jostling and breaking.

At home, the shells may be replaced in alcohol until they are sufficiently loosened to be cleaned, or until you have time to get to them.

Treatment of specimens with broken-off soft parts

Those specimens not completely cleaned of the soft parts may be propped up with the spire down, or placed so in glass jars or plastic containers. Pour formaldehyde into the shell, turning it back and forth to be sure the formaldehyde gets into the spire. Put a lid on the container, or stuff the aperture with cotton to prevent or

149

delay evaporation. Tape the operculum and station number to the container or to the shell if it is a large one. Leave for a week, rinse with water and dry.

Where there are facilities for freezing, this method is used with fine results by many collectors:

1. Wash off sand and mud. Rinse, drain, dry.

2. Put specimens in plastic containers padded with paper towels to absorb any water left in them, and to protect the lips of fragile shells. Large specimens may be put in heavy paper cartons if plastic containers are not available.

3. Put containers in the freezing compartment for two full days. They may stay without harm as long as it is convenient for the collector. I cleaned successfully one specimen frozen for ten years!

4. When removed from the freezer or freezing compartment of a refrigerator, allow to thaw thoroughly with the aperture down.

5. The soft parts may be shaken out, forced out with a jet of water, or gently rolled out with a pointed instrument. Freezing shrinks the soft parts so that they are loosened at the point of attachment.

6. If the soft parts do not come out completely, follow the directions already given for this problem.

With some shells, particularly cowries (*Cypraea*) and similarly shaped species, the remaining soft parts can be scratched loose and flushed out. It may take time to do a thorough job.

Freezing is the safest cleaning method for species with a high gloss all over or around the aperture. Next best is the alcohol-soak. Do not boil.

With very large specimens you may have to combine two methods: freezing and hanging. Because of the narrow aperture of *Cassis* (helmet shells) it is difficult to insert your instrument far enough into the large foot at the right angle to twist-and-roll it out successfully. For different reasons, other large specimens may be troublesome.

Freezing is an ideal way of dealing with chitons, which often curl or hump before they can be bound securely to a wooden tongue depressor for drying or preserving in alcohol. Put them in a shallow pan or platter with enough sea water to cover. When they are relaxed, pop the container in the freeze compartment. The mollusks die conveniently sprawled out and later are bound with no difficulty to the wooden splints.

This method is a good one for species whose shells will not be hurt. It should not be used by novice collectors for shells with a high gloss or mother-of-pearl lining.

1. If a number of shells are to be boiled together, use cotton bags to keep separate those from different collecting stations. If you are not experienced enough to know one operculum from another, one specimen to a bag will avoid getting the shells and opercula mixed. Sometimes the opercula fall off in the boiling or cooling stage.

2. Use a stainless steel or enameled pot. An enameled bucket may be needed for many or large specimens.

3. Cover the shells with cold water.

4. Bring to a boil *slowly*, using moderate heat to the simmer stage.

5. Allow two or three minutes of actual boiling for large shells, less than that for small ones.

6. Remove container from burner.

7. Allow the water to cool *gradually* until the specimens may be taken out, one at a time, by hand. The soft parts come out more easily when they are warm. Don't boil too many specimens at one time because the last shells to be cleaned may have cooled too much.

8. Follow the procedures already described for removing the soft parts, cleaning each shell and operculum; and keeping the station number with the shells in whatever container they are kept until cataloging time.

HANGING, BAHAMIAN STYLE

Large specimens may be tied to a low limb or clothesline with the aperture down. As the animals die, they "droop" and "run"; and after about two days they can be pulled out, leaving the shells clean. So it goes in theory; in practice it does not always work out so. The shells must be tied securely and some shapes are easier than others to secure. The heavy cord must not cross the aperture because it will impede or halt the "drooping."

The shells must be high enough to keep small animals from making off with the meat—because the operculum will go with the tasty foot.

Another version of hanging is to put a cord with a slip-knot around the foot, and hang from a low limb with the shell down. As the animal droops, the cord must be shortened to keep the shell above ground, yet near enough for the shell not to be hurt if the muscular attachment pulls loose and the shell drops.

If it is possible to do so, it is good to put a slip-knot around the foot of a large specimen to be frozen, if the shell has such a narrow aperture that it is hard to work the thawed flesh out with a tool.

When the shell is clean, completely or partly, follow the described procedures for cutting off the operculum, washing, and packing with the station number.

Large shells from which the flesh has not come entirely out may be put in sacks weighed and tied, or in crab traps, and put back in the sea, wherever convenient. Before long the flesh can be shaken out. This is safe in the sea. *Do not* try this in a bucket or jar of water. Unless the water is constantly changed, the acids of decomposition will ruin the shells.

To avoid the risk of losing the opercula of "hanging" specimens, I usually cut them off; wrap each in paper; and tape, or tie, it to a wooden tongue depressor. If you have plastic vials large enough, the opercula could be put in them. On the wrapping paper, or on a slip in the vial, I write the station number and a note identifying the shell to which the operculum belongs. For example:

No. 2. Largest (or next large, small, smallest) *Cassis tuberosa*.
or:

No. 1. *C. tuberosa* with 3 dark spots on lip.

No. 3. *C. tuberosa* with barnacles on spire.

FURTHER CLEANING FOR APPEARANCE

Whether you do anything more to your shell after curing or removing the soft parts is a matter of taste. Professional malacologists usually want the specimen as much in its natural state as possible; and so do many serious amateurs. This may mean treating the shell with oil or paraffin to preserve the periostracum, which often cracks and flakes off. Generally scientists do not try to remove encrustations like barnacles or coralline algae.

Many experienced amateur collectors prefer a compromise. Some

Cassis tuberosa—(*King Helmet*). *Note the flattened spire, the thickened outer lip and the short upcurved siphonal canal. This species is found where there is a generous supply of its preferred food: the white-spined sea urchin. A larger, closely related Cassis of Florida (*Clench's Helmet*) feeds on big heart urchins; and a small member of the same family,* Phalium granulatum *(*Scotch Bonnet*) likes sand dollars. An observant collector found that, before drilling a hole in the thin-shelled urchin, the predatory Clench's Helmet removed the spines from the area it planned to bore. Then, without discomfort, the snout could be thrust through the hole to eat the soft contents of the urchins.*

specimens in each lot are left in the natural state with the periostracum preserved; others are cleaned to show the colors, patterns, and texture.

Some collectors coat their shells inside and out with mineral oil, let them stand for a day or so, and then blot off the excess. Sometimes it may be necessary to put facial tissue or paper toweling in the bottom of the compartment—box or "tray"—in the cabinet drawer, for specimens that are still oily. If the periostracum is thick and fibrous, it is not always easy to blot off excess oil.

Some collectors recommend the addition of a small amount of chloroform and neat's-foot oil to mineral oil, thinking this is better than pure mineral oil. Chloroform is available at drugstores but a physician's prescription is necessary for purchase. Adult beginners in shell collecting would probably have no trouble obtaining a prescription from a family physician; but a young beginner would need the assistance and supervision of an older person.

Coating with paraffin is another way of preserving the periostracum. Since this method involves the use of a kind of alcohol which is flammable, young collectors should not attempt it without the help of an adult. The method is:

1 cake of paraffin (the kind used for sealing homemade jelly. Obtainable at grocery stores.)

1 pint Xylol (This may have to be ordered from a chemical supply house. Ask your druggist.)

Cymatium caribbaeum—Caribbean Cymatium. This small triton is confined to the warmer portions of the Western Atlantic. Its range is from Bermuda, southern Florida, the West Indies and Central Mexico south to Bahia, Brazil. Note the interesting outer coat, periostracum.

Put these ingredients in a pot large enough to dip your specimens in and set the pot in a large container filled with boiling water. *Do not heat the mixture on the stove.* Stir with a clean stick until the paraffin is melted. Hold your specimen with large kitchen tongs in such a way that you can dip all parts of the shell covered with periostracum. Set the specimen aside on a tray covered with paper toweling. The Xylol evaporates, leaving a thin coat of paraffin on the periostracum.

The periostracum of some species is interesting but not pretty. That of others is very pretty and a shell stripped of it looks skinned —as, of course, it is. Since this outer coat may be removed any time, try at first cleaning only one or two specimens of a kind. If you clean all, you may regret it later.

LAUNDRY BLEACH

Dipping or soaking shells in a laundry bleach, full strength or diluted, will remove the periostracum. Thin coats come off quickly; thicker ones take longer. Shells heavily coated with dried marl and various encrustations have to be soaked for several hours or overnight.

Whether dipped or soaked, each shell should be thoroughly scrubbed under running water to remove all of the bleach. Heavily encrusted shells with a roughly sculptured surface may need scrubbing with a stiff brush (tooth or nail brush) and gentle scraping with a fine, sharp tool. Barnacles can be chipped and scratched off.

Try first a mixture of 1 part of bleach to 1 part of water, and a quick dip or short soak. Wash well, dry, examine. Perhaps this is all that is needed. If not, try a second treatment with the same proportion, or a stronger mixture.

Some people think the use of laundry bleach in any proportion damages the shell by fading the colors. We have not had this experience. The alternative treatment, suggested by some who dislike the use of laundry bleach, is too dangerous to suggest for novices.

Scrubbing with soap and water will clean opercula. The operculum may be stored in a vial with the shell in your cabinet; or it may be lightly glued to a bit of cotton and fitted into the aperture of the shell. Be sure to get it right side out and right end up.

Cleaning not only seems like a lot of work, it is a lot of work.

155

What hobby does not require work of some kind? Think of the constant care required for boats and motors, boots and guns, tennis courts and rackets. The sailors, fishermen, hunters, and players accept the work as part of the game or sport. Collectors do too.

No. 22

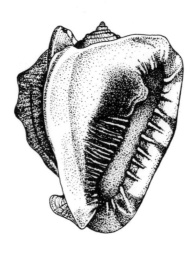

Chapter 23
Cataloging

As soon as your specimens are ready for the cabinet, catalog them! Postponed, the job soon becomes an appalling task for which there never seems to be time.

Each shell is numbered, just as a book in a library is. The same number is then posted in a notebook or ledger and followed by information about where the shell was collected.

The best cataloging system, the one used by most museums, is the most simple. Without regard to what kind they are, the specimens are numbered consecutively as they are obtained. Few private collections reach 10,000 entries in the ledger used as a catalog, so one never deals with more than four numerals. With the other systems, like giving a number to each family and numbering from one up with each, you soon reach six or seven spaces, counting the dash, and often there is not room enough on a specimen for so long a number.

Every shell does *not* receive a different number, but every "lot" of shells *does*.

A "lot" is *one* batch or tray of specimens of *one* species from *one* collecting place regardless of the number of specimens; and *each specimen in the lot receives the same catalog number.*

If on a certain day you collect eight *Conus mus* (Mouse Cone) along the shoreline of Lobster Key, all would receive the same number, say 319. A single *Conus mus* found on Coconut Key would be number 320. It is the same species, but from a different place or "locality." Six *Cypraea* (cowries) and a pair of *Murex* (rock shells), of the same species, collected that same day would receive the next numbers—321 for all the *Cypraea*, 322 for both *Murex*.

Use a fine-point pen and India ink. The number is usually put on the lip just inside the aperture. Cataloging is so essential to a fine collection that if you are among those amateurs who consider catalog numbers "disfiguring," try to conquer your feeling. If you prefer, put the number in a less conspicuous place, but put it on the shell. Some collectors put the numbers on small squares of waterproof adhesive tape and stick them on the shells. This is not good practice because in some climates the squares come unstuck, and may be lost. It is safer to mark the shell, and to do so is the mark of a sound scientific attitude on the part of the amateur collector.

Be sure the specimen is dry before attempting to mark it. Mistakes can usually be rubbed off with a small stick tipped with cotton and dampened with water or laundry bleach. Dry *thoroughly* before remarking.

Avoid chalky places. These will make the ink run as it does on a blotter. If the whole shell is chalky, use a pencil with a hard lead and sharp point.

If the specimens are very small the number may be put on the plastic or glass vial, or bottle in which the specimens are kept.

Your catalog should be a sturdy ledger or notebook which lies

Cittarium (formerly Livona) pica (West Indian Top Shell). This handsome black-and-white shell is abundant throughout the West Indies on rocky coasts in exposed places as well as in tide pools, and under loose slabs of rock. It is more abundant below low water mark. The columella and the interior of the aperture are glazed with iridescent white. The cupped operculum, trapdoor, translucent and a rich brown in color, fits the aperture snugly. Note the deep, round umbilicus (hole in the base) (Fig. 1.) and the catalog numbers on aperculum.

The animal is an interesting one to observe and photograph. The head is large bearing a blunt snout (proboscis); double-lobed eyestalks, with a single eye in the outer lobe and a long tentacle between the lobes. When the snail is fully extended, the mantle may be seen. On one side sawtooth lobes stand upright. Fossil specimens may be found in Bermuda.

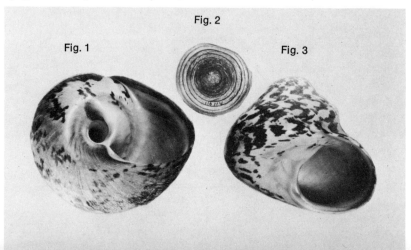

Fig. 2

Fig. 1

Fig. 3

flat when opened. Do not skimp on size. Your catalog can make or break your collection. There should be plenty of room in it for recording all important information about where and when each specimen was found. This information follows the catalog number for the "lot," and should be in your Field Notes.

The paper should be smooth and of good quality. Instead of ink, which may fade, some collectors prefer using a sharp, rather hard pencil on smooth paper. Soft pencils and rough paper are a bad combination where lasting legibility is important.

Write or print clearly. Don't make the letters so small that they are hard to read. If the lines of your ledger are close together, skip a line between each entry.

In addition to the information which goes in your catalog, it is good practice to put the essential information on a small card or slip of paper which is kept in the box or container for each lot. These slips make it unnecessary to thumb through your catalog when looking over your collection or showing it.

Once your specimens are properly cataloged you are free of many worries. You are no longer nervous when guests look at your collection, fearing that a shell picked up for examination may be returned to the wrong box, and thus separated from its all-important card with the locality data. If this should happen to you a number of times, you will be convinced of the need for cataloging. The catalog is your permanent record.

No. 23

Chapter 24
A Good Collection

What is a "good" collection?

To many amateurs the worth of a collection is judged by the number of beautiful, foreign and rare shells.

Professional malacologists and knowing laymen think it unfortunate that amateurs are generally so impressed with the rare, the strange, the perfect that they ignore the common. Scientists urge collectors to develop an interest in common species easily collected in shallow water. A comprehensive collection of shells from one area, with an excellent catalog, would be more likely to win a blue ribbon from the "pros" than one composed of beauties and oddities from all over the world.

For example, a woman who runs a souvenir shop in a small Atlantic coast resort has such a comprehensive collection of local species that biology professors from a famous nearby university frequently take visiting foreign scientists to see it.

Good local collections can supply valuable information for professional research. Museums do not always have enough material on hand for a comprehensive study of a group, or family, of shells; and must borrow from other museums and reliable private collectors.

In a 1958 study of the Pinnidae (pen shell family) in the western Atlantic, the Department of Mollusks at Harvard had gathered plenty of material from Florida and Texas but had nothing from the north Gulf coast. My husband and I were asked to lend all the material we had from the Alabama-Mississippi coast. We had nothing because these bivalves are large, the largest being about nine or ten inches long and five or six inches wide. Thus they take up a great deal of cabinet space. They are very brittle and easily broken. They are very common, not pretty, and to us, in the early collecting years, of little interest. The family was represented in our

Argonauta hians (Brown Paper Argonaut). From a sandspit at La Paz, Baja, California; in the author's collection. John Lewis Stage

collection by one specimen of each of the three Gulf and Caribbean species, all of which had come from southern Florida.

Our efforts to obtain living or dead specimens from other Alabama collectors and fishermen were unsuccessful. Time was flying. The research was nearly done, with the north Gulf coast still a blank.

At the eleventh hour, a fellow collector phoned to say that there was a young girl in his store who had just picked up a living pen shell (one of the dark species called *Atrina*) on the beach, and he thought he had persuaded her to let me have it for the researchers. I offered a "pretty" shell in exchange. The girl and her mother arrived to choose one of several shells which I put out for her to look at. They were all "glamor" shells, appealing to most young collectors. She picked each one up, examined it carefully, put it down, and repeated the performance.

I began glamorizing. "The round, shiny bivalve is called the Sun-and-Moon Shell, red on one side, white and yellow on the other." "Vikings used snail shells like these for drinking cups. They were mounted on stands of gold or silver." "This is an abalone shell. The mother-of-pearl is often used for inlay and costume jewelry. Sometimes they produce odd-shaped, one-sided pearls which may be quite valuable."

It was the wrong approach. I had made a choice more difficult.

At the end of an hour she had come to no decision. Her mother was embarrassed; I, exasperated. Unless I got the *Atrina* to the post office before the fast-approaching closing time, it would never reach Boston alive. In desperation I told the girl to take *all* of the pretty shells and excused myself to wrap the bivalve for mailing, hoping I could get by with my highhandedness. I did.

By airmail, the shell arrived in Boston the next morning and was put in an aerated observation tank beside a specimen from Florida. One valve of each specimen had been removed without injury to the animals. The color and shape of the organs were so different that the scientists realized the two shells were different species and that one was not just a variation of the other. The muscle scars and other shell features showed the specimens from Texas were identical with the living shell from Alabama. The species was called *Atrina seminuda*. (*Atrina* means dark; *seminuda* refers to the nearly spineless valves.) The other North American *Atrina* are as rough as graters, one with tiny spines, one with big spines.

161

In the handsomely published report of this study there is a paragraph listing the names of all the institutions and individuals who made the research possible by giving or lending specimens. Among them are the names of the little girl and the other Alabama collectors who had helped in obtaining the valuable living bivalve.

Having learned our lesson about the value of common shells, we explored our coast for this species, found it in another locality, and filled this gap in our collection. We also sent specimens to several museums.

In building your own collection, remember that shallow water Cinderellas may become stars in the cast of a scientific show.

No. 24

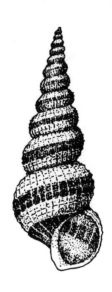

Chapter 25
Storing,
Displaying,
Exhibiting

Protected from dust and direct sunlight, most shells retain their beauty indefinitely. Generally collectors start with small displays in glass-topped tables or cupboards with shelves and glass doors. In time, collections outgrow these storage places. More space becomes necessary. Cabinets with drawers are the solution, but just what kind of cabinet is governed by one's budget. Your cabinet might be an old chest with fairly shallow drawers; it could be a new custom-made cabinet. Study the diagrammatic drawing in Dr. Abbott's *American Seashells*.

However it is housed, this is the time for your collection to grow up, to become a "study" collection, not just an accumulation of souvenirs. This kind of collection is not as dull as it may sound; it can be as attractive as it is orderly.

A study collection is one in which all specimens are arranged by scientific groups. For most amateurs this means: class, family, and species. The drawers are fitted with boxes of various sizes which the collector can make of heavy paper, buy in special sizes, or accumulate. The job of fitting them together to accommodate specimens of varying sizes and numbers can be quite a job. Doing it well is a challenge.

Most of the specimens will be univalves and bivalves. You may start with either class. The families should be arranged systematically, that is, in order of their classification, starting with those which are biologically the most primitive, least specialized groups, and ending with the most complex. Use as a guide the arrangement in any authoritative book of identification.

The small classes SCAPHOPODA (tusk shells), AMPHINEURA (chitons) and CEPHALOPODA (nautiluses, argonauts, spirulas) may follow the large ones: GASTROPODA (snails) and BIVALVIA (bivalves). The last drawer is often reserved for unidentified specimens.

If the collection is not too large or if there is ample space, the shells can be arranged attractively in the drawers. They may be kept in plastic boxes or cardboard boxes with glass or cellophane tops—spread out only one deep, or stacked. Glass-topped and plastic boxes may be ordered in varying sizes from biological supply houses. Those with cellophane tops may be accumulated. Notepaper, Christmas cards, and many toilet articles come in such boxes. Specimens may be kept in topless boxes lined with blue or white cotton, felt, or blotting paper, whose colors show the shells off to best advantage. However you display your specimens, don't sacrifice good collecting practice to "prettiness." Keep your "lots" separate.

A study collection does not preclude having attractive displays of shells also, if that appeals to you. Once cataloged, your shells may be displayed in any of the popular decorative ways without fearing the loss of data cards stuffed into apertures or taped on specimens which have not been numbered. Your cabinets of drawers may be topped with a glass display case; lighted display cases may be built into bookcases; shallow cabinets with glass shelves may be built into walls.

For public exhibits, cataloged specimens may be removed from the drawers by the dozens or hundreds, with no worry and no extra effort on the collector's part except the necessary wrapping for safe transportation to and from the exhibit hall.

In arranging your home displays and public exhibits, follow some kind of plan. Don't arrange your shells in a haphazard way. Whatever your theme, keep the classes separate.

You might display local shells: bivalves to the right, snails to the left, or in separate cases.

You might display worldwide shells by families: Pectinidae, the beautiful scallops; Muricidae, the dramatic spiny snails; Cypraeidae and Conidae, the universally loved cowries and cones. It is interesting and instructive to study the variations and similarities within a family.

Your displays might be keyed to the various uses to which the shells have been put:

Those used for pearl inlay or ornaments.

Those used as a source of purple dye.

Those used as money or from which shell "money" was made.

Those used as charms, as horns, or as sacred or domestic vessels.

One of the most interesting displays I ever saw was an exhibit of fossil and "recent" (living today) shells, side by side. Many were identical. Some were enough alike to identify as to genus but not as to species.

There are endless ways of grouping shells to catch the attention of people who don't know much, if anything, about shells; and are delighted to learn in an easy way. Your exhibit might make someone else eager to join "the shell game."

No. 25

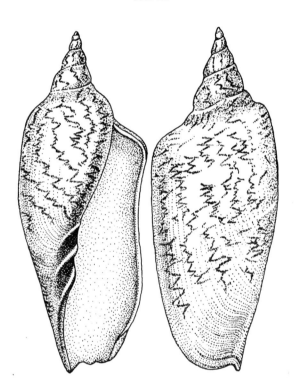

Chapter 26
Adding to
Your Collection

Adding to your collection is easy if you live in a good collecting area, or are able to vacation in many good areas. You exchange your duplicates with collectors who have shells you don't have.

But what if you don't live on a good coast and are limited in your travel? What then? For those with a will, there are ways.

How does a beginner begin? Join a shell club. There are often meetings devoted to swapping or trading. Show what you have and see who is interested. Information about current clubs (some come and go) may be found in *Sources of Information About Mollusks,* compiled by and obtainable from:

THE DIVISION OF MOLLUSKS

UNITED STATES NATIONAL MUSEUM

WASHINGTON, D. C. 20560

If there is no club in your area, join one of the well-established old clubs—Broward, Houston, New York, San Antonio—which publishes a newssheet or letter. Through the secretary you can find members your age, or others interested in exchanges.

There has been organized recently *The International League for Young Shell Collectors* (ILYSC) "to encourage greater interest in the study of shells among young people"; "the exchange of shells and ideas internationally"; and "to furnish vocational advice to those interested in malacology as a career."

The professional advisers are a galaxy of stars: Drs. William J. Clench, R. Tucker Abbott, Kenneth Boss and Mr. Morris K. Jacobson of the U.S.A. Representing South America, there is Brother Mark Ross, S.J. of Peru.

Since there can be no meetings, the members keep in touch with each other through their mimeographed paper: *The Young Shell Collector's Quarterly.* The editors and officers at present represent Lima, Peru; Watertown, Massachusetts, U.S.A.; and Belgium. "We welcome all inquiries," the new group announced in its first annual report to the American Malacological Union, the "AMU" to old members.

Address inquiries to:

Mrs. Edwin S. Hicks, Public Relations

7170 Lucky Drive, N.

Jacksonville, Florida 32208

This is a wonderful way of making friends with a common interest, all over the world.

Or you may invest in one of the directories listing collectors all over the world, who are interested in exchanging shells. Code letters show their special interests: certain kinds of shells (marine, freshwater, land, fossil); classes, families; shells from specific areas, or worldwide. In one directory the ages of all collectors under 20 are given in parentheses so that prospective traders may contact others of their own ages and degrees of experience. The members are listed by states, in the United States; and by countries.

If you don't have enough fresh-from-the-sea shells to trade, you might make inquiries about fossil collecting in your area and offer fossil for recent specimens. Some inland areas are rich in fossil shells. However, collecting, cleaning and preserving techniques all are different from those for living species; also many names are not the same. This type of trade demands knowledge of two fields of study. They are closely related and knowledge of the two is vastly interesting and quite a challenge. As you see from the directory listing of interests, there are many collectors of fossil shells.

You might exchange stamps for shells. If you aren't already a stamp collector, this also means you will have to master two hobbies. Exchanging in two fields is complicated, but fun. A good many collectors enjoy it. Many started by saving stamps from exchange boxes from foreign collectors.

RULES FOR EXCHANGING

There are rules for exchanging shells. Don't ignore them. Even in this time of increasing informality, good manners matter. Good manners endure from generation to generation, varying only slightly from country to country, because they are based on common sense and courtesy.

Some years ago I received a poorly wrapped, crushed box in

167

which there were a handful of faded, broken shells. The sender's address was illegible. It had been scrawled on rough, used wrapping paper with a soft pencil. I could make out one name "Joie." Boy? Girl? Were the shells intended as a gift? Were they sent with the expectation of a return package? I had no way to find out bcause of the unreadable address. The sender thinks I am very rude and ungrateful; or worse, not honest.

The sender was at fault, not I.

The shells were worthless even before they were broken in transit, but the innocent sender did not know it.

If you send shells as a gift, enclose a card saying so. If you want to be thanked, PRINT your name and address with care.

If you want to exchange shells, be courteous enough to ask if the person you want to exchange with is: (1) interested in exchanging; (2) interested in what you have to offer; and, (3) has material to offer you in return. Exchanges, like marriages of old, *have to be arranged*. You must write a letter asking about the other person's willingness to exchange, even when you get the name from a list of people interested in trading, generally. The person may not be eager to trade with you. Advanced collectors may be very choosy. You must explain what kind of shells you wish to swap, or enclose lists of what you have to offer and what you would like in return. You must say whether or not you have good locality data for your specimens.

You must be willing to send a sample, if requested; or to return what you have received and accept the return of what you have sent, if the other person is not satisfied. Reliable dealers do this. "Satisfaction guaranteed, or your money back."

PACKING

Proper packing is essential. If you want to know how to pack shells, ask permission to watch in the shipping department of a store which sells glass and china.

Yes! Shells have to be packed just as carefully as glass goblets. Each one is wrapped, then rewrapped with folded, crushed paper. And then each goblet is buffered from the one below and on the sides, by wads of crushed paper, strips of paper or excelsior. There is padding between the glass and the carton. And the carton, note, is a sturdy one; or a lightweight one inside a sturdy one.

168

Pack a shell as you would a goblet.

Wrap the carton neatly in unwrinkled wrapping paper. Tape or tie it well. Don't tie "grannies." Learn how to tie square-knots. Look in a dictionary or a scout manual for illustrations and directions. Use sturdy cord. Gummed tape which cannot be ripped off without ripping the wrapping paper is a great help for shipment within our country. Packages going abroad can't be taped. They must be tied so that they can be opened by customs officials; and a declaration must be made. Postal officials will explain these regulations.

PRINT your address. PRINT the address of the person to whom you are sending. If the shells sent are rare and of recognized monetary value, insure your box against breakage or loss.

Otherwise mark your package:

MARINE MOLLUSKS

SCIENTIFIC SPECIMENS

NO COMMERCIAL VALUE

and trust to luck. In some countries, unfortunately, a commercial evaluation is an invitation to corrupt postal employees to open and keep the contents. Because of this, our government, and some others, will not insure packages going to a number of countries.

Many collectors enjoy buying shells from commercial dealers. Once your name appears on the membership list of a shell club, lists from dealers will begin to arrive. All the specimens are listed by Latin names; knowing them is essential. Dealers don't bother with common names because they are meaningless to their foreign customers. Dealers' prices vary greatly. It is wise to compare them before buying. *Van Nostrand's Standard Catalog of Shells* is most valuable in helping you judge fair prices. It is compiled by experienced professionals and laymen and well illustrated.

Frequently dealers make enticing special offers.

One dealer runs a *Shell-of-the-month Club,* which is a popular feature with beginners. For a small sum each month, a subscriber will be sent a particular shell. Usually it is a common but attractive species. Beginners enjoy the "surprise" of these monthly packages.

Some dealers offer boxes of assorted shells for beginners. Another dealer offers dredged material (sand, mud and whatever is in it) by the bushel, not sorted or graded, but from varying depths. Prices increase with the depth from which material comes. There is no guarantee that there will be shells, good shells, or rare shells. The mixtures range from "student" and "general," from shallow and

Ancistrosyrinx elegans—Elegant Star Turret. This rare, two-inch turret shell dredged from very deep water off Key West is another example of the breath-taking beauty of many shells. The half-inch Common Star Turret (Ancistrosyrinx radiata), nearly as beautiful, is commonly dredged in water less deep, but too deep for most amateur dredgers. This species could be a prize in bagged, dredged, deep-water material offered for sale.

fairly deep water with no detailed locality data, to mixtures from much deeper water with exact data required by serious collectors. The prices range at present from $10 to $30 a bushel, plus freight.

Biology classes and groups of friends make joint purchases, working out their own systems for fair distribution. Sorting material provides hours of interest—and the exciting possibility of finding a real treasure. Considering the cost of a dredging expedition and the frequency of shell-less hauls, the prices are not excessive.

"Spring cleaning" sales of dealers often offer real bargains.

Some beginning collectors living inland enjoy shell-hunting in secondhand stores, at bargain sales, auctions and antique shops. The shells found in such places do not have the locality data considered essential by advanced collectors, but they can be a challenge to beginners. In trying to identify them by comparing with illustrations in field guides, the beginner can learn quite a bit. It is not difficult to spot family, and often easy to pin down the species because the shells turning up in such shops are usually those which have been popular for years as souvenirs of travel: cowries (Cypraea); "cameo" shells (Cassis); Chambered or Pearly Nautiluses (Nautilus pompilius); Green Turban shells (Turbo marmoratus); Pearly Top Shells (Trochus niloticus) and many kinds of abalones (Haliotis). Some of these shells may be found in their natural state, but often the outer coat has been polished off to show the pearly undercoat. Some of the Cassis (cameo shells) are elaborately engraved with classical scenes, and some of the Cypraea (cowries) are etched with the Lord's Prayer.

170

There is no one way, no "right" way of going about shell collecting. The direction taken depends as much on point of view and interest as on opportunity.

Those primarily interested in beauty will collect specimens chosen for shape, color, texture. Their specimens will be displayed as objects of art. And why not, if this is what such collectors find exciting? It may add to their pleasure, however, to know something about the natural history of their oceanic gems.

Those with an interest in history and the uses to which men have put shells could assemble a fascinating collection of shells which have been used as money, charms, ornaments or vessels. Such a collection might not have much appeal to malacologists, but it certainly would to anthropologists. And in such a collection locality data for specimens would add infinitely to its value. The source of shells throws light on cultural and trade relations.

For those with a general interest in nature, and a specific interest in shells, there *is* a right and a wrong way of collecting. These people will find greater satisfaction in a "study" collection than in an assemblage of specimens without information about their origins. Be it small and limited in range, or huge and far-ranging, make it a superior collection from a scientific point of view. Let it be worthy of a blue ribbon from the "pros."

If you plan to collect shells, plan to collect books, too. You will need many, you will want more. Several good ones are available in paperback. More expensive ones are available from libraries or shell clubs. You may wish to look them over before investing. Some are listed on page 173. A more comprehensive and carefully evaluated list is included in *Sources of Information About Mollusks* (see page 166). If possible, visit the museums and aquariums listed on page 177.

The shell game is an exciting game. Play it—and good luck!

No. 26

Suggested Reading

PRIMARILY FOR IDENTIFICATION

Pocket size for your beach bag:

A Field Guide to the Shells of Our Atlantic and Gulf Coasts
and
A Field Guide to the Shells of the Pacific Coast and Hawaii by Percy
Morris. Boston. Houghton Mifflin Company. Peterson Field Guide
Series. Hardback. Excellent for areas covered. Color plates and
halftones.

Seashells of the World, A Guide to the Better-Known Species by R.
Tucker Abbott. New York. A Golden Nature Guide, Golden Press.
Paperback. Excellent. In several languages. All illustrations in
color.

How to Know the American Marine Shells by R. Tucker Abbott.
New York. New American Library. A Signet KEY Book. Inexpensive, authoritative, well illustrated.

To borrow from your library or to buy:

American Seashells by R. Tucker Abbott. Princeton, New Jersey.
D. Van Nostrand Company. A basic work on species of both coasts.
Splendid introduction on the Phylum Mollusca and collecting.
Color plates, halftones, line drawings.

Seashells of Tropical West America by A. Myra Keen. Stanford,
California. Stanford University Press. The introduction gives the
history of the fauna, describes typical and unusual collecting areas,
presents a forceful plea for conservation. Paragraphs introducing
each major division offer a liberal education. Color plates, halftones,
line drawings.

Caribbean Seashells by Germaine L. Warmke and R. T. Abbott.
Wynnewood, Pa. Livingston Publishing Company. Indispensable
for the area. The first chapter offers information about when,
where and how to collect; describes each major island or group of
islands and what may be found there. Color plates, halftones, line
drawings.

173

Queensland and Great Barrier Reef Shells by D. F. McMichael and O. H. Rippingale. New. Twenty-nine exquisite color plates.

Australian Shells by Joyce Allan. Boston. Charles Branford Company. Fully illustrated.

The Shell Book by Julia Rogers. Boston. Charles Branford Company. Worldwide. A reprint of an old favorite with an appendix by Dr. Harald Rehder, United States National Museum, giving the current names.

Check your library or bookstore for other books on special areas or shell families. There are many.

Write to: United States National Museum, Division of Mollusks
        Washington, D. C. 20560

for its list of useful books about mollusks for amateurs and students.

INTRODUCTORY WORKS

Sea Treasure, A Guide to Shell Collecting by Kathleen Yerger Johnstone. Boston. Houghton Mifflin Company. For beginners. Beautiful color plates and drawings by Rudolf Freund and Rene Martin.

Molluscs by J. E. Morton. Inexpensive edition by Harper Torchbooks, New York. Harper & Row. Also hardback. Diagrammatic sketches clarify discussion of the six classes. Highly recommended.

ABOUT SEA LIFE ON SHORES AND REEFS

The Edge of the Sea (Atlantic Coast) by Rachel Carson. Boston. Houghton Mifflin Company. A scientist writing like a poet.

Between Pacific Tides by Edward F. Ricketts and Jack Calvin. Revised by J. W. Hedgpeth. Stanford, California. Stanford University Press. Most informative.

Common Seashore Life of Southern California by J. Hedgpeth and Sam Hinton. Excellent, illustrated inexpensive booklet. Healdsburg, Calif. Naturegraph Co.

Southern Seashores, A World of Animals and Plants by William M. Stephens. New York. A Holiday House Science Book, Holiday House, 1968.

Reef and Shore Fauna of Hawaii. Bernice P. Bishop Museum, Honolulu, Hawaii 96819. Special publication. Second edition. Seventy-five figures of Mollusks.

174

The Ocean Island (Inagua, Bahama Islands) by Gilbert Klingle. New York. Dodd, Mead & Co. A shipwrecked naturalist explores a little-known island. Exciting adventures.

The Sea Shore (England) by C. M. Yonge. Most interesting and instructive. New York. William Collins Sons & Co., Ltd.

Wonders of the Great Barrier Reef (Australia) by T. C. Roughley. Sydney. Angus & Robertson. Beautiful illustrations. Informative, delightfully informal.

The Great Barrier Reef and Adjacent Islands by Frank McNeill, Curator, Australian Museum, Sydney. General text. Keith Gillett, A.R.P.S., Photographer. Magnificent illustrations. Excellent, concise text.

The Coast of Coral by Arthur C. Clarke. New York. Harper & Row. 1956. Interesting descriptions of the Great Barrier Reef and pearl-diving in the Torres Straits.

FOR EXCHANGING AND BUYING
Directory of Conchologists of the World by Richard E. Petit, P. O. Box 133, Ocean Drive Beach, South Carolina 29582.

Collectors Directory by P. R. Page, Box 16291, Phoenix, Arizona 80501.

Standard Catalogue of Shells. Edited by Robert J. L. Wagner and R. Tucker Abbott. Princeton. D. Van Nostrand Company, Inc. 221 illustrations. Gives actual market evaluations of thousands of shells of the major groups; common and Latin names; geographical ranges; world size records; quick regional check lists with price ranges; lists shell clubs of the world; and some dealers. Most useful for extensive exchanging and buying.

FOR CLEANING
How To Clean Seashells by Eugene Bergeran, Director, Marine Biological Associates, Balboa, Canal Zone. Privately Printed. Inexpensive. Latin names are used exclusively. Familiarity with them is essential for understanding the instructions. Order from: Ormand McGill, 581 Forest Avenue, Palo Alto, Calif. 94301.

FOR COLLECTING TECHNIQUES
How To Collect Shells, A Symposium, published by the American

Malacological Union, available for a modest price from the Secretary. This booklet is filled with useful information from skilled collectors. It covers a number of specialized techniques. Collectors interested in dredging will find several excellent articles covering this very interesting and productive method of collecting.

Museum Exhibits

The great collections of the country are research centers open to qualified scholars, but generally closed to the public. Only those having or planning displays for the public are included here.

UNITED STATES NATIONAL MUSEUM, Hall of Life in the Sea. A part of the Smithsonian Institution, Washington, D. C.

AMERICAN MUSEUM OF NATURAL HISTORY, Central Park West at 79th Street, New York, N. Y.

FIELD MUSEUM OF NATURAL HISTORY, Roosevelt Road and Lake Shore Drive, Chicago, Ill.

MUSEUM OF ZOOLOGY, University of Michigan, Ann Arbor, Mich.

CARNEGIE MUSEUM, 4400 Forbes Avenue, Pittsburgh, Penna.

SAN DIEGO NATURAL HISTORY SOCIETY, Balboa Park, San Diego, Calif.

LOS ANGELES COUNTY MUSEUM, 900 Exposition Boulevard, Los Angeles, Calif.

SANTA BARBARA MUSEUM OF NATURAL HISTORY, 2559 Puesta Del Sol Road, Santa Barbara, Calif.

PACIFIC GROVE MUSEUM OF NATURAL HISTORY, Forest and Central Avenues, Pacific Grove, Calif.

OAKLAND MUSEUM, 906 Fallon Street, Oakland, Calif.

WASHINGTON STATE MUSEUM, Olympia, Wash.

BERNICE P. BISHOP MUSEUM, Honolulu, Hawaii

OTHER EXHIBITS

BEAL-MALTBIE SHELL MUSEUM, Rollins College, Winter Park, Fla.

SIMON DE MARCO FLORIDA MARINE MUSEUM, north of Fort Myers, Fla.

SANIBEL-CAPTIVA SHELL FAIR, Sanibel Island, Fla. Held annually for more than twenty-five years, some time in March.

AQUARIUMS

These institutions feature some living mollusks:

MIAMI SEAQUARIUM, Rickenbacker Causeway, Miami, Fla.

THOMAS WAYLAND VAUGHAN AQUARIUM-MUSEUM, La Jolla, Calif.

THE STEINHART AQUARIUM, Golden Gate Park, San Francisco, Calif.

TACOMA AQUARIUM, Point Defiance Park, Tacoma, Wash.

Bibliography

ABBOTT, R. TUCKER: *American Seashells*—New York, D. Van Nostrand Co., Inc., 1954.

——, *Seashells of the World*—New York, Golden Press, 1962.

——, "The Venomous Cone Shells," *The Science Counselor*—Pittsburgh, Duquesne University Press, December 1950.

ALLAN, JOYCE: *Cowry Shells of World Seas*—Melbourne, Georgian House, 1956.

BATTEN, ROGER L.: "The Need to Classify," *Natural History*—New York, American Museum of Natural History, 1958.

CLARKE, ARTHUR C.: *The Coast of Coral*—New York, Harper & Brothers, Publishers, 1955.

CLENCH, WILLIAM J. and KONDO, YOSHIO: "The Poison Cone Shell," *American Journal of Tropical Medicine*—Vol. 23, No. 1, January 1953.

——, *Republished in Occasional Papers on Mollusks*—Vol. 1, No. 7, March 15, 1946—The Department of Mollusks, Museum of Comparative Zoology, Harvard University, Cambridge, Mass.

COOKE, REV. A. H.: *Molluscs*, Vol. 3; *The Cambridge Natural History*—New York and London, The Macmillan Company, 1895.

FRIES, T. M.: *Linnaeus*, adapted by Benjamin D. Jackson—London, H. F. & G. Witherby, 1923.

HAGBERG, KNUT H.: *Carl Linnaeus*, translated from the Swedish by Allen Blair—London, Jonathan Cape, 1952.

HARDY, ALISTER C.: *The Open Sea*—Boston, Houghton Mifflin Co., 1956.

HEDGPETH, JOEL and HINTON, SAM: *Common Seashore Life of Southern California*—Healdsburg, Calif., Naturegraph Company, 1961.

IDYLL, C. P.: *Abyss, The Deep Sea and the Creatures That Live in It*—New York, Thomas Y. Crowell Co., 1964.

KEEN, A. MYRA: *Sea Shells of Tropical West America*—Stanford, Calif., Stanford University Press, 1958.

Kohn, Alan J.: "Studies on Food and Feeding of the Cone Shells, Genus *Conus*," Bulletin No. 22, Annual Report of the American Malacological Union, December 1955.

————, "Feeding in *Conus striatus* and *Conus catus*," Proceedings of the Hawaiian Academy of Science, 31st Annual Meeting, 1955–56. Published by the University of Hawaii.

————, "Piscivorous Gastropods of the Genus *Conus*," Contribution No. 78, Hawaii Marine Laboratory, Proceedings of the National Academy of Sciences, Vol. 42, No. 3, pp. 168–171, March 1956.

————, "Recent Cases of Human Injury Due to Venomous Marine Snails of the Genus *Conus*," Hawaii Medical Journal, July-August 1958, Vol. 17, Hawaii Medical Association.

————, "The Ecology of *Conus* in Hawaii," Contribution 113, Hawaii Marine Laboratory, University of Hawaii, *Ecological Monographs*, 29:47–90, January 1959.

Lemche, Henning: "A New Living Deep-Sea Mollusc of the Cambro-Devonian, Class Monoplacophora," *Nature Magazine*— Washington, D. C., February 23, 1957.

Lindroth, Sten: *Swedish Men of Science 1650–1950*—Stockholm, The Swedish Institute, Almquist & Wiksell, 1952.

Macpherson, J. Hope: *New Gastropods from North Australia*— Melbourne, Memoirs of the National Museum, No. 24, December 1959.

Mayr, Ernst, Linsley, E. G., and Usinger, R. L.: *Methods and Principles of Systematic Zoology*—New York, Toronto, London, McGraw-Hill Book Company, Inc., 1953.

McNeill, Frank: *The Great Barrier and Adjacent Isles*—Sydney, Australia. Published by the Coral Press Pty. Ltd.

Minor, Roy Waldo: "Marauders of the Sea," *The National Geographic Magazine*—Washington, D.C., National Geographic Society, August 1935.

Newell, Norman D.: "Questions of The Coral Reefs," Part I, March 1959; "Biology of The Corals," Part II, April 1959, *Natural History*—New York, American Museum of Natural History.

Nordenskiold, Eric: *The History of Biology* (Lamarck), New York, Alfred A. Knopf, 1928.

PACKARD, ALPHEUS S.: *Lamarck, The Founder of Evolution, His Life and His Work with Translations of His Writings on Organic Evolution*—New York, London and Bombay, Longmans, Green, and Co., 1901.

PELSENEER, P.: *Mollusca*, Vol. 5 of *A Treatise on Zoology*, edited by Ray Lankester—London, Adam and Charles Black, 1906. Agents, The Macmillan Company, New York.

PHILLIPS, CRAIG and BRADY, W. H.: *Sea Pests, Poisonous or Harmful Sea Life of Florida and the West Indies*, A Special Publication of the Marine Laboratory, University of Miami, University of Miami Press, 1953.

POIRIER, HENRY: *Marine Mollusca of the Eastern Coast of North America, Their Names and Meanings*—Published and Copyrighted 1952 by the author.

RICKETTS, ED. F. AND CALVIN, JACK: *Between Pacific Tides*, Revised by Joel W. Hedgpeth, Stanford University Press, 1952.

ROGERS, JULIA E.: *The Shell Book*—New York, Doubleday, Page and Co., 1908. Second Edition, Boston, Charles Branford Co., 1951.

SCHENK, EDWARD T. and McMASTERS, JOHN H.: *Procedure in Taxonomy*, Third Edition; enlarged and in part rewritten by A. Myra Keen and Siemon William Muller, Stanford, Calif.; Stanford University Press, 1956.

SCHROCK, ROBERT R. and TWENHOFEL, WILLIAM H.: *Principles of Invertebrate Paleontology*, Second Edition—New York, Toronto, London, McGraw-Hill Book Company, Inc., 1953.

THE NAUTILUS—Editors and Publishers:

Horace B. Baker, Charles B. Wurtz, R. Tucker Abbott
Mrs. Horace B. Baker, Business Manager
11 Chelten Road, Havertown, Pennsylvania 19083.

KLINE, GEORGE: "Notes on the Stinging Operation of *Conus*"—Vol. 69, January 1956.

MOORE, DONALD R.: "Observations of Predation on Echinoderms by Three Species of Cassidae"—Vol. 69, January 1956.

TURNER, H. J., JR.: "How Clam Drills Capture Razor Clams"—Vol. 69, July 1955.

JOHNSONIA—*Monographs of the Marine Mollusks of the Western Atlantic*. Edited by William J. Clench, Published by the

Department of Mollusks, Museum of Comparative Zoology, Harvard University, Cambridge, Mass. 02138.

CLENCH, WILLIAM J.: "The Genus *Conus* in the Western Atlantic"—Vol. 1, No. 6, December 5, 1942.

———, and TURNER, RUTH D.: "The Family Melongenidae in the Western Atlantic"—Vol. 3, No. 35, January 30, 1956.

———, and TURNER, RUTH D.: "The Family Cymatiidae in the Western Atlantic"—Vol. 3, No. 36, December 1957.

TURNER, RUTH D. and ROSEWATER, JOSEPH: "The Family Pinnidae in the Western Atlantic"—Vol. 3, No. 38, June 28, 1958.

INDO-PACIFIC MOLLUSCA—*Monographs of the Marine Mollusks of Tropical Western and Pacific Oceans.* Edited by R. Tucker Abbott. Published by The Department of Mollusks, Academy of Natural Sciences of Philadelphia, Philadelphia, Pennsylvania 19103, U.S.A.

Vol. 1, No. 1. Introduction. *Ecology* (listing information desirable for superior locality data); *Reef Terminology* (with a cross section); and a map of Indo-Pacific Province, March 31, 1959.

Vol. 1, No. 7. *The Genus Terebellum* (Gastropoda: Strombidae) by Peter Jung and R. Tucker Abbott, May 15, 1967.

SEA FRONTIERS—Magazine of the International Oceanographic Foundation. Institute of Marine Science, University of Miami, Florida 33149.

STEPHENS, W. M.: "The Exquisite Argonaut"—Volume II, No. 3, May–June, 1965.

IDYLL, C. P.: "Living Fossils of the Deep"—Volume II, No. 3, May–June, 1965.

Illustrations

Endpapers: The Natural History Museum of the Emperor Ferdinand III of Germany. The engraving appeared in *Historia Naturale di Ferrante Imperato,* published in Venice, 1672, and was based on the woodcut in the Naples edition of 1599.

COLOR PLATES

Identification of Tailpieces
by Harry Inge Johnstone

No. 1: Page 2
Thais planospira—*Flatly-spiraled Rock Shell*
(*thā'is planō'spīrà*)
The yellow-brown, rounded "back" of this shell is often camouflaged
with marine growths or deposits. The other side is like white china. Both
outer and inner lips are ornamented with dark red ridges. The line
crossing the depressed white area is black. This attractive and uncommon
snail is found from the tip of Lower California to Peru, and in the
Galapagos Islands, on rocks at extreme low tide. From a specimen in the
Johnstone collection from the Galapagos Islands.

No. 2: Page 4
"You pause to marvel . . ."
Left: Trivia pediculus—*Coffee-Bean Trivia*
Middle: Vermicularia spirata—*West Indian Worm Shell*
Right: Crucibulum striatum—*Striate Cup-and-Saucer Shell*

No. 3: Page 9
Trachycardium muricatum—*Sharp-scaled Yellow Cockle*
Showing the interlocking teeth of the hinge through the parted valves.
After Johnsonia.

No. 4: Page 17
Solutiscala vermetiformis—*In the "wentletrap" family: Epitoniidae*
This one-quarter-inch rare, deep-water shell dredged off Brazil is shown
as an example of a loosely coiled spiral. The Latin words from which
the name was made mean: loose, free, not bound; ladder or staircase;
worm-like in form. After Watson in Johnsonia.

No. 5: Page 21
Cardium costatum—*Ribbed Heart Shell or Cockle*
An Indo-Pacific species. East coast of Africa.

No. 6: Page 28
Nautilus pompilius—*Chambered Nautilus showing the shell; the lifting,
leathery hood, which serves as an operculum (trapdoor); the emerging
tentacles which surround the mouth; and one eye.*

No. 7: Page 33
Isocardia cor—*Equal-sided Heart Shell*
In the Johnstone collection. From the Mediterranean coast of Spain. Col-
lected by Elsy Thöni-Vogt of Switzerland.

No. 8: Page 38
Scaphella junonia—*Juno's Volute*
Left: The unique "left-turn" specimen found at Naples, Florida.
Right: A normal specimen from the Johnstone collection.

No. 9: Page 45
Aequipecten irradians amplicostatus—*Broad-ribbed Atlantic Bay Scallop*
This edible scallop is found from central Texas to Mexico and Columbia.
It is common in Texas. Note the straight hinge line, the nearly equal
"ears," and the black bit of resilium in the triangular pit.

No. 10: Page 51
One of the pair of telescoping water glasses.

No. 11: Page 57
Thatcheria mirabilis—*Miraculous Thatcheria*
The broad "shoulder" emphasizes the spiral form of this beautiful, deep-
water turret shell of Japan. This is the largest species of several hundred
in the family Turridae.

No. 12: Page 60
Murex (Chicoreus) monodon—*Single-tooth Murex (juvenile)*
In the Johnstone collection. From Elizabeth Blair Grigg, who collected
it in an isolated area of the northwest coast of Australia. The name was
suggested by a single, tooth-like projection on the outer lip pointing in
the direction opposite to the back-curved, ornamental spines.

No. 13: Page 70
Tellidora cristata—*White Crested Tellin*
From a specimen in the Johnstone collection. Note the well-impressed
muscle scars, and the indentation called pallial sinus, *where the retracted*
siphons lie.

No. 14: Page 80
Janthina janthina—*Purple Sea Snail*
The living animal showing the snout (proboscis); tentacles; the modified,
cap-like foot and the bubble raft. From a sketch in the author's field
notes.

No. 15: Page 87
Cyphoma signatum—*Fingerprint Cyphoma*
A West Atlantic species. From a sketch in the author's field notes, show-
ing the distinctive pattern of the mantle, the foot, tentacles and siphon.

No. 16: Page 95
Melo amphora—*Giant Jar, Melon or Bailer Shell*
A member of the volute family, Volutidae, found around the Indian
Ocean and Australia; showing the enormous foot, too large to be with-
drawn completely, and the uplifted siphon. After T. C. Roughley in
Wonders of the Great Barrier Reef.

No. 17:   Page 113
Conus striatus—*Striated Cone*
The beautiful shell of the deadly, fish-eating mollusk.
From a specimen in the Johnstone collection.

No. 18:   Page 122
Pugilina morio
After Johnsonia

No. 19:   Page 134
Left: *Base of* Cypraea guttata—*Great Spotted Cowry.*
White spots speckle the orange-colored humped "back." The teeth on the base are dark red ridges and run some way up the side of this beautiful and rare species of the southwest Pacific. Only seventeen specimens are known.
Right: *Base of* Cypraea spadicea—*Chestnut Cowry*
The white base of this species contrasts with the colorful hump. Found from Monterey, California, to Cedros Island, Lower California.
Center: *Base of* Cyphoma signatum—*Fingerprint Cyphoma*
The family to which this species belongs, Ovulidae (Egg Shells) is closely related to that of the cowries, Cypraeidae. Found in the lower Florida Keys to the West Indies.

No. 20:   Page 138
Nerita peloronta—*Bleeding Tooth Shell*
The name was suggested by the red spot around the prominent teeth of the inner lip. A west Atlantic species. From sketches in the author's field notes.
Left: *Under side of the shell showing the teeth and operculum.*
Middle *and* right: *Showing the shell, divided foot, eyes and tentacles.*

No. 21:   Page 145
Guildfordia triumphans—*Triumphant Star Shell*
Showing the clockwise spiral of most snails. Found in East Asia. Common in Japan in deep water.

No. 22:   Page 156
Cassis tuberosa—*King Helmet Shell*
From a specimen collected by the Johnstones on one of the Bahama Out Islands. Note the broad, raised, white teeth on the outer lip; and the narrow, ridge-like teeth on the inner margin of the parietal shield.

No. 23:   Page 159
Jumala crebricostatus—*Thick-ribbed Buccinum (bŭk' sĭ-nŭm)*
(yōō'mä-lä krē'brĭ-cŏs-tā-tŭs)
A deep-water shell from Alaska seen in few private collections. Note the neat catalog number on the lower part of the outer lip. (Jumala means: a god. Crebri means: close-set.) After Dall.

No. 24:   Page 162
Amaea mitchelli—*Mitchell's Amaea or Wentletrap.*

In 1950 this beautiful species was known only from beachworn specimens found at Galveston and Matagorda Island, Texas. The operculum was unknown. It is thin, dark brown, and fits the aperture snugly. Besides living and freshly dead beach specimens, the Johnstones have others dredged off the Mississippi delta. Mature specimens are two to two and a half inches long.

No. 25: Page 165
Zidona dufresnei—*Dufresne's Zidona*
The cream-colored mantle mottled with dark green produces a shell which ranges in color from yellowish to orange, irregularly patterned with reddish-brown, zigzag lines. Some shells are long and slender (from around five to seven and a half inches); others are shorter and broader. After Donovan, Naturalists Repository, 1823, from Johnsonia and specimens in the Johnstone collection.

No. 26: Page 171
Harpa major *(formerly* ventricosa) Ventricose Harp Shell
One of the most beautiful of the twelve currently known species in the genus Harpa. All but one, Harpa crenata of the Panamic Province, are found in the Indo-Pacific Province. Harp shells do not produce an operculum.

JOHN LEWIS STAGE is known for his photographic approach to land and nature. His advertising and editorial assignments, many of them overseas, have won high awards including the New York Art Directors Gold Medal for editorial photography. His work has been published in most foreign and American magazines and in particular *Holiday*, to which he has been a contributor for years.

WILLIAM M. STEPHENS, an avid amateur oceanographer and marine biologist when he graduated from the University of Tennessee, did graduate work in the field of ocean life at Miami University. Since then he has written numerous scientific papers and three excellent books, besides exploring subtropical waters, on and below the surface. He is currently managing editor of *Oceanography International*.

HARRY INGE JOHNSTONE, B. Arch., F.A.I.A., a practicing architect, has continued his interest in drawing and painting since he was art editor of the Cornell *Widow*. As the active collecting partner of the author, his knowledge of seashells is evident in the authenticity of the pen-and-ink drawings used for the tailpieces and some other parts of the book.

Index

194

About the Author

KATHLEEN YERGER JOHNSTONE admits that she has been "shell-shocked" for nearly twenty years. During all the time she and her architect husband were bringing up their three sons in Mobile, Alabama, which is still their home, shell collecting was a family hobby and the determining factor in most of their vacation plans.

They have collected shells from Alabama east, around Florida, up the Atlantic coast to Virginia, on several of the Bahama Islands, and on the coasts of Texas and California. They have visited many museums and aquariums. Their library is loaded with volumes on malacology, the study of mollusks, and their correspondence bears postmarks from all over the world as foreign and distant friendships developed through sharing a mutual interest.

Mrs. Johnstone gives generously of her rich store of knowledge and experience, in other fields besides malacology, through talks to literary and volunteer service groups, historical associations, and at the Birmingham Museum of Art; in articles published in *Holiday* and other magazines; and in her fine previous book *Sea Treasure*.